Process Improvement Using Six Sigma

Dear Mike,

With Love

from

Rama

Also available from ASQ Quality Press:

The Certified Six Sigma Black Belt Handbook, Second Edition
T. M. Kubiak and Donald W. Benbow

The Certified Six Sigma Green Belt Handbook
Roderick A. Munro, Matthew J. Maio, Mohamed B. Nawaz, Govindarajan
Ramu, and Daniel J. Zrymiak

Six Sigma for the New Millennium: A CSSBB Guidebook, Second Edition
Kim H. Pries

5S for Service Organizations and Offices: A Lean Look at Improvements
Debashis Sarkar

*The Executive Guide to Understanding and Implementing Lean Six Sigma:
The Financial Impact*
Robert M. Meisel, Steven J. Babb, Steven F. Marsh, and James P. Schlichting

Applied Statistics for the Six Sigma Green Belt
Bhisham C. Gupta and H. Fred Walker

Statistical Quality Control for the Six Sigma Green Belt
Bhisham C. Gupta and H. Fred Walker

Six Sigma for the Office: A Pocket Guide
Roderick A. Munro

*Lean Six Sigma for Healthcare: A Senior Leader Guide to Improving Cost and
Throughput,* Second Edition
Chip Caldwell, Greg Butler, and Nancy Poston.

Defining and Analyzing a Business Process: A Six Sigma Pocket Guide
Jeffrey N. Lowenthal

Six Sigma for the Shop Floor: A Pocket Guide
Roderick A. Munro

Six Sigma Project Management: A Pocket Guide
Jeffrey N. Lowenthal

Lean Kaizen: A Simplified Approach to Process Improvements
George Alukal and Anthony Manos

To request a complimentary catalog of ASQ Quality Press publications,
call 800-248-1946, or visit our Web site at http://www.asq.org/quality-press.

Process Improvement Using Six Sigma

A DMAIC Guide

Rama Shankar

ASQ Quality Press
Milwaukee, Wisconsin

American Society for Quality, Quality Press, Milwaukee 53203
© 2009 by ASQ
All rights reserved. Published 2009
Printed in the United States of America
15 14 13 12 11 10 09   5 4 3 2 1

Library of Congress Cataloging-in-Publication Data

Shankar, Rama, 1956–
    Process improvement using Six Sigma : a DMAIC guide / Rama Shankar.
        p. cm.
    Includes index.
    ISBN 978-0-87389-752-5 (soft cover : alk. paper)
    1. Six sigma (Quality control standard) 2. Total quality management.
    3. Process control. 4. Reengineering (Management) I. Title.

    HD62.15.S477 2009
    658.4'013—dc22   2008052670

ISBN: 978-0-87389-752-5

Publisher: William A. Tony
Acquisitions Editor: Matt T. Meinholz
Project Editor: Paul O'Mara
Production Administrator: Randall Benson

ASQ Mission: The American Society for Quality advances individual, organizational,
and community excellence worldwide through learning, quality improvement, and
knowledge exchange.

Attention Bookstores, Wholesalers, Schools, and Corporations: ASQ Quality Press
books, videotapes, audiotapes, and software are available at quantity discounts with
bulk purchases for business, educational, or instructional use. For information,
please contact ASQ Quality Press at 800-248-1946, or write to ASQ Quality Press,
P.O. Box 3005, Milwaukee, WI 53201-3005.

To place orders or to request a free copy of the ASQ Quality Press Publications
Catalog, including ASQ membership information, call 800-248-1946. Visit our
Web site at www.asq.org or http://www.asq.org/quality-press.

Printed in the United States of America

 Printed on acid-free paper

Quality Press
600 N. Plankinton Avenue
Milwaukee, Wisconsin 53203
Call toll free 800-248-1946
Fax 414-272-1734
www.asq.org
http://www.asq.org/quality-press
http://standardsgroup.asq.org
E-mail: authors@asq.org

Om
to
My guru
My mother
My family

Table of Contents

List of Figures and Tables

Read Me First

This book is intended to be a guide for the quality practitioner as he or she works through an improvement project. While there are many self-help books out there, here the topic is discussed in a way so as to remove the fear of Six Sigma and worrying about statistics. The primary purpose of this book is process improvement, and we need to keep that front and center in our minds. Improvement ideas still come from team members, the only difference here is that data are collected and analyzed along the way to validate our assumptions and ensure that we are on the right path.

Topics in the book are discussed only from the perspective of the importance of the information in arriving at conclusions, and not from a mathematical angle.

Examples are provided in each section to assist in understanding the subject matter. Calculations were made using Minitab software; however, you can use any statistical software to do the math.

You may also decide to pick and choose certain tools to support your conclusions or decisions and not necessarily undertake a full-fledged improvement project.

I hope you have fun, and good luck!

Acronym List

CAPA—corrective and preventive action
cGMPs—current good manufacturing processes
CI—continuous improvement
COGQ—cost of good quality
COPQ—cost of poor quality
COQ—cost of quality
CTD—critical to delivery
CTQ—critical to quality/regulations
CTS—critical to satisfaction
CTx—where "x" is substituted for Q, D, or S
DMAIC—Define–Measure–Analyze–Improve–Control
DOE—design of experiments
DPU—defects per unit
FMEA—failure mode and effects analysis
GCPs—good clinical practices
MSA—measurement systems analysis
QMS—quality management system
r—correlation coefficient
RPN—risk priority number
R-sq—coefficient of determination
SIPOC—supplier, input, process, output, customer
SME—subject matter experts
SPC—statistical process control
TPS—Toyota Production System
VOC—voice of the customer
VOP—voice of the process
VSM—value stream map

Introduction

In order to stay competitive, organizations need to continuously improve their processes. The purpose of this book is to provide the quality practitioner with the necessary tools and techniques with which to implement a systematic approach to the process improvement initiative using the Six Sigma methodology.

This systematic approach takes into account the following principles:

- Customer needs and functional area needs are understood and met.

- Leveraging the knowledge of subject matter experts (SMEs) and team members to improve the process.

- Arriving at team consensus on root cause(s) of problems.

- Risk is managed by addressing all compliance issues.

PROCESS IMPROVEMENT METHODOLOGY AND THE QUALITY MANAGEMENT SYSTEM

The process improvement methodology works within the framework of an established *quality management system* (QMS). There are many types of QMSs that are in place today, unique to different industries. For example, ISO/TS 16949 is the QMS for the automotive industry, AS9100 for the aerospace industry, current good manufacturing processes (cGMPs) for those businesses that have manufacturing processes regulated by FDA, ISO 9001 for a business/service organization, and the list goes on. Two of the components of a robust QMS are *corrective and preventive action* (CAPA) and *continuous improvement* (CI) that are driven by analysis of data.

There are many types of continuous improvement methodologies, such as:

- Gut feeling—don't sit on your hands, do something

- Plan–do–check–act (PDCA) methodology

- Lean manufacturing principles or Toyota Production System (TPS) implemented through kaizen

- Six Sigma implemented through Define–Measure–Analyze–Improve–Control (DMAIC)

The DMAIC methodology takes a problem that has been identified by the organization and utilizes a set of tools and techniques in a logical fashion to arrive at a sustainable solution(s). The resultant solution(s) will minimize or eliminate the problem, placing the organization in a competitive position.

So how do you identify a problem that requires solving? Before we answer this question, we must first understand some fundamentals: What is a QMS? Who are the customers and suppliers? What are their requirements?

In order to understand what a QMS is, we must first understand what a system is in the context of the organization. A *system* is similar to the maze of pipes, all connected, starting at a reservoir and ending with the tap at your house. When the tap is opened, the water flows, meeting your requirement for running water. Similarly, various processes within the organization are linked/connected to translate the *voice of the customer* (VOC) into delivery of a product/service that meets the customer's expectations. Breaking the definition down further, a process is just a collection of activities that come together in a predetermined sequence that transforms inputs into outputs, utilizing resources to effect the transformation. Resources can further be categorized into groups such as personnel, equipment, method, measurement, material, and environment. A QMS, therefore, is the management of the processes and their linkages by the organization to ensure that the output meets the quality requirement dictated by the customer.

It is to be understood here that a customer can be the end user or a chain of customers who utilize the output of the system or process. The customer of one process can also be the supplier to another process or, in other words, the output of one process is the input to another process. Therefore, understanding customer requirements and communicating them in a clear manner upstream to suppliers will ultimately ensure that the resultant output of the system, whether it is a product or service, meets those customer requirements. See Figure 1.

Regardless of the type of industry you work in, the organization is measured by the customer based on the yardstick of quality, price, and delivery.

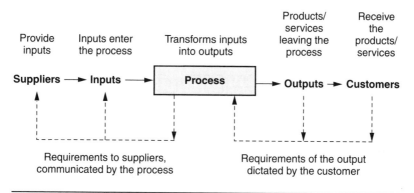

Figure 1 The process model.

Quality translates into conformance to requirements, *price* relates to the actual cost incurred for delivering the product or service, and *delivery* with time to market. As the saying goes, "The early bird catches the worm," and needless to say if you can satisfy the customer on all three fronts, your organization will be successful.

Customer requirements may be stated in the regulations/specifications governing the industry, or unstated but understood as necessary by the organization based on their experience. The job of the organization, therefore, is to understand these requirements and ensure that the activities within the process are designed in such a manner that the requirements are met as the input is being transformed along the way to becoming an output. Any gap in the translation of these input requirements manifests itself as a defect in the output.

By collecting data on the key metrics (quality, price, and delivery) and analyzing such data the organization can identify areas for continuous improvement.

The Six Sigma methodology used for process improvement is the Define–Measure–Analyze–Improve–Control methodology, also known as DMAIC. By taking a problem through the DMAIC phases in a collaborative setting with a team of personnel, the resultant solution addresses the root cause. If the process improvement methodology is considered as a process in itself, then the input to the process improvement methodology is the problem, the output is the solution to the problem, and the process box in the methodology can be decomposed to Define, Measure, Analyze, Improve, and Control (see Figure 2).

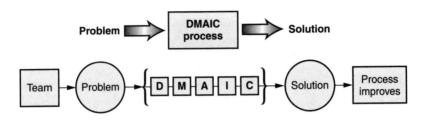

Figure 2 The DMAIC process.

I
Define

PURPOSE OF DEFINE PHASE

The Define phase ensures that the problem/process selected to go through the DMAIC process improvement methodology is linked to the organization's priorities and has management support. The Define phase starts with identifying a problem that requires a solution and ends with a clear understanding of the scope of the problem and evidence of management support, who authorize the project to move forward through a commitment of resources. First, we need to understand some concepts:

- Most problems in the operational side of an organization are associated with a process or set of activities. Therefore problem solving for the purpose of this book is synonymous with "process improvement project" or "problem solving project." These phrases may be used interchangeably but convey the same meaning.

- The organization does not necessarily have to be facing a problem in order to use the DMAIC methodology. A project may be selected purely for the purpose of continuous improvement (CI) in order to be competitive in the marketplace.

- If a problem already has an identified solution and an action plan, then it is an implementation project and is not a process improvement project. Implementation projects do not follow the DMAIC methodology. All you need to do is work through the action plan already put in place.

HOW DO YOU IDENTIFY PROJECTS FOR IMPROVEMENT?

There are many ways to identify a project for improvement; for example, upper management may assign a project based on strategic criteria,

1

or CAPA may indicate trends or problem areas. One of the tools used to identify a candidate for a problem-solving project is known as *cost of quality* (COQ).

COQ allocates costs incurred by the organization's activities into two categories: the cost of conformance and the cost of nonconformance. Conformance costs, also known as the *cost of good quality* (COGQ), can be broken down into costs associated with appraisal and prevention activities. Simply put, *appraisal costs* are related to inspection/QC activities, documentation review, calibration, and so on, and *prevention costs* are related to activities such as error-proofing, supplier audits, training, validation, planning, and so on.

Nonconformance costs can be broken down into costs associated with *internal failure* and *external failure*. Nonconformance costs, therefore, are costs associated with the failure to meet customer requirements, and are also known as the *cost of poor quality* (COPQ). Internal failure costs are typically reported as scrap, rework, reprocessing, recheck, redesign, downtime, and so on, while external failure costs manifest as returns, allowances, recalls, lawsuits, warranty claims, penalties, complaints, and so on. "Gating the defect" is a term used to differentiate between internal failure and external failure. To use an analogy, you lock the barn door to prevent the horse from running away. The organization should typically try to identify quality issues regarding its products and services in-house, before they reach the customer.

A COQ graph is a bar chart with cost on the *y*-axis and cost category on the *x*-axis. The cost categories are represented by four vertical bars, each bar depicting the sum of costs incurred for prevention, appraisal, internal failure, and external failure categories for the reporting period.

Regardless of whether or not the organization has a formal COQ program, management and employees usually have a good understanding of where the internal failure and external failure costs lie. Problems requiring a solution should therefore be identified first from the external failure cost category and then from the internal failure cost category. This ensures linkage to business results and bottom-line improvement.

HOW DO YOU PICK A PROJECT?

A tool used to help narrow down a problem in either the external failure or internal failure categories of COPQ is the Pareto chart. A Pareto chart can further break down each of the categories by cause of failure, product/service offering, type of customer, and so on. A Pareto chart is useful for picking a project because:

- It helps the organization get a clear picture of where the greatest contribution can be made.

- The principle suggests (in most situations) that a few problem categories (approximately 20 percent) will present the most opportunity for improvement (approximately 80 percent).

- It prioritizes problems so that the major problems can be identified.

A Pareto chart is a bar chart where the values being plotted are arranged in descending order. Typically, the *y*-axis shows the frequency of occurrence, but it can also represent cost. The *x*-axis is labeled with group names such as cause, part number, service type, or customer type.

Since the tallest bar on the chart represents the biggest problem, the data dictate how problems should be prioritized. Keep in mind that you may need to do multiple levels of Pareto charts to look at a problem from different viewpoints (see Figure 3). For example, a product or service offering may have a high frequency of failures, but when looked at through the lens of cost, the same problem may appear in the fifth or sixth category. Consider graphing multiple levels of Pareto charts, and if a problem shows up with a relatively high frequency in every level (say in the top three), then that is your ideal candidate for a problem-solving project.

From the charts in Figure 3, we can conclude that this organization is having a problem with bad data, and the highest frequency is on Thursday.

HOW DO YOU SCOPE YOUR PROJECT? THE SIPOC DIAGRAM

Once the problems have been prioritized and one selected for improvement, your next task is to determine the scope of the problem. Defining scope helps you prevent "scope creep" and diluting your effort. The multiple levels of Pareto charts provide you with clues to the nature of the problem— whether it is critical to quality/regulations (CTQ), critical to delivery (CTD), or critical to satisfaction (CTS)—and links it to the customer and process where the problem is manifest. (Note: Herein after these will be generally referred to as CTx, where "x" is substituted for Q, D, or S.)

SIPOC stands for *supplier, input, process, output,* and *customer.* A SIPOC diagram takes a "high-level" view of the process. It does not need to show any decision points, only blocks indicating high-level activities (see Figure 4). A value stream map (VSM) may also be used in place of a SIPOC diagram. The SIPOC or VSM can be used to identify the area of the process where the problem originates.

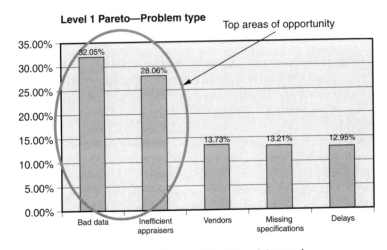

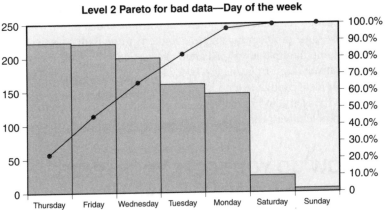

Figure 3   Example of multiple levels of Pareto charts.

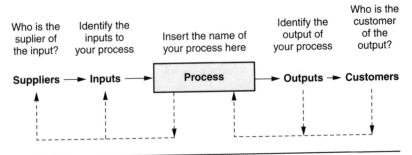

Figure 4   SIPOC diagram template.

- Start out by identifying the process within the organization that provides the product or service that the customer is unhappy about.

- Then, use the CTx from the Pareto chart to further narrow down the problem to the few steps in the process that are responsible for creating the CTx. These few steps (usually about seven or eight steps) represent the scope of your problem-solving project.

- Now that you know the scope, this sets the boundaries of your project, that is, the start point and the end point activities in the process being considered for improvement.

- The start point is the first activity within the scope and the end point is the last activity within the scope.

- Anything entering the boundary from the prior step is considered a supplier, and anything leaving the boundary and going to the next step is considered a customer.

You can now pull all this information together and easily create a SIPOC diagram for your project. This is now the sole focus of your problem-solving project.

Following is a simplified example of a SIPOC for "going to work in the morning" (see Figure 5):

- Your boss expects you to be at work on time.

  - Customer is your boss/organization

  - Customer requirement is that you should be at work on time

- In this example the supplier/input is you, the employee, who is going through the process of "going to work in the morning."

  - Start point of the process is "Get out of bed"

  - End point of the process is "Transport to work"

- The output of the process is "Employee at work on time"

- If you want to improve your "on-time" arrival at work, these are the steps that need to be analyzed to identify causes of delays.

Figure 5   SIPOC diagram for "going to work in the morning."

ASSEMBLE THE PROCESS IMPROVEMENT TEAM

Use the following criteria to select team members for the process improvement project:

- Select subject matter experts (SMEs) from the process where the problem has been identified.

- You may want to include an "outsider," that is, a person from another department who does not know much about the process. This person will usually ask the uncomfortable questions and challenge the status quo since they are often trying to learn what is going on.

- Team members should represent different levels in the organization (exempt/nonexempt) to bring different perspectives to the problem.

- The team leader may either be appointed by management or can be the process owner or a person within the organization who is skilled at facilitation and has working knowledge of the tools and techniques.

- Try to limit the number of team members to fewer than eight.

- Hold team meetings on a weekly basis and take minutes (see Figure 6).

Some organizations may have resident Green Belts or Black Belts who lead such projects.

Do not forget to create a communication plan (see Figure 7), which defines how the actions of the process improvement team will be communicated to the rest of the organization.

CREATE A PROJECT AUTHORIZATION/ CHARTER DOCUMENT

At this point, the problem that has been selected and scoped for improvement will be handled as a project. A *charter* document can now be created, which is an agreement between the problem-solving team and management (see Figure 8).

Meeting Minutes

Meeting title				
Meeting purpose				
Date of meeting		Time		
Team lead		Scribe		
Attended				
Not able to attend				

Agenda topic(s)	Outcome(s) (decisions, deliverables)
1.	
2.	
3.	
4.	
5.	

Summary of discussion/decisions

Action items	Person responsible	Due date
1.		
2.		
3.		
4.		
5.		
Date/time of next meeting		

Figure 6 Example of a meeting minutes template.

Communication Plan

Audience	Media	Topic of discussion/ key message	Responsible person	Frequency of communication	Comments

Figure 7   Example of a communication plan template.

Charter

Prepared by	
Date issued	
Project name	
Purpose of project	
Business case/need (Business reasons for the project)	
Team members	
Estimated duration of the project	
Functional areas involved	
Suppliers to the process	
Project scope (start and end)	
Not included in scope	
Project goal(s) (What is it intended to achieve?)	
Estimated cost $	
Timeline and estimated project completion date	
Estimated savings $	
Final deliverable(s)	
Team leader signature	
Management signature	

Figure 8   Example of a simple charter document template.

Since the problem selected for improvement was identified from the internal/external failure category in the COPQ, it now becomes easy to estimate the monetary savings based on the project goal, using the charter document.

END OF DEFINE PHASE

You have now reached the end of the Define phase in the DMAIC process improvement methodology:

- Use the End of Define Phase Checklist to ensure that all of the Define phase activities have been completed.

- Collect objective evidence for items on the checklist and use them as a guide to present management with monthly updates.

- Follow good record keeping practice (whatever method works for your organization, electronic or hard copy).

- Celebrate the end of Define phase activities with your team.

End of Define Phase Checklist		
Items	**Place (✓) in box to indicate completion**	**Comments**
COPQ or Pareto charts		
Problem selected for improvement		
SIPOC created		
Team leader and team members identified		
Meeting held with team		
Communication plan completed		
Charter document created • Problem statement • Scoped project • Estimated savings • Goal • Timelines		
Meeting held with management • Roadblocks encountered		

II

Measure

PURPOSE OF MEASURE PHASE

The purpose of the Measure phase is to gather baseline information about the process that has been identified as needing improvement. Baseline information about the process is used to better understand what exactly is happening in the process, customer expectations, and where the problems lie.

In the Measure phase you first start collecting data and quantifying the problem. How many times has the process failed to meet some CTx factor required by the customer? At this point, remember, you are merely collecting data in a passive manner, that is, using historical data (if any) to gather information. You need these data to quantify improvement in the Control phase of the DMAIC methodology and show management that you have made a positive difference!

It may not come as a surprise to find that your organization, like many others, does not have much data, in which case an effort must be made to study the process and spend a little bit of time gathering data from the "current state" before proceeding to make changes.

Four things need to be completed in the Measure phase:

- Understanding the activities in the process by creating a process map of the current state

- Understanding where the risk lies in the process by performing a failure mode and effects analysis (FMEA)

- Determining how well the process meets customer expectations by calculating process capability

- Assessing the measurement system to ensure that reported data are accurate and there is no inherent variation due to the way in which data are collected

DEVELOP AN UNDERSTANDING OF YOUR PROCESS—CREATING PROCESS MAPS

There are many types of process maps that are used in an organization depending on the level of detail that you would like to know. Examples of different types of maps are:

- SIPOC diagram.

- Value stream map (VSM).

- $Y = F(X)$ map, used in Six Sigma DMAIC methodology. Y is the output and X's are the inputs; that is, the output (the product or service) is a function of the process inputs.

- Flowcharts.

For the purpose of process improvement, the $Y = F(X)$ map is commonly used, and will be described below. However, your organization may use the VSM instead. It really does not matter which of these maps is used as long as you capture all the information about the process.

The flowchart is a tool generally used to create a procedure or work instruction and captures more details and decision points in the process. Since we are really interested in understanding the factors that influence our process, and not the "who, what, when, where," and so on, this is an optional tool that is better used in the Control phase to create procedures or work instructions as necessary.

The $Y = F(X)$ process map is drawn with input from the process improvement team. For the process selected for improvement, expand on the SIPOC diagram that you drew in the Define phase. Start out by documenting the steps in the process. Keep the steps at a "bird's eye" view of the process:

- *Identify six to eight high-level steps in the process.* It is all right if you have more than eight steps or fewer than six. Remember, it is your process and the main purpose here is to develop a team understanding of what is happening in the process.

- *Identify the input coming into the process, that is, entering the "start point" of your process.* This includes anything entering the process, provided by the supplier process. One important assumption the team needs to make here is that anything entering the process meets requirements. Otherwise, the team will end up spending a lot of time pointing out problems related to the supplying process. This assumption helps the team focus on the scope and also look at the process from the perspective of what could possibly go wrong in the steps under review.

• *Identify the inputs to each step.* The inputs are known as the "*X*'s" of the process step. A simple way to make sure that all the inputs have been considered for each step is to utilize the brainstorming methodology. At the end of the brainstorming session, group all the inputs into the following categories under each step:

   – *Personnel.* These are persons who have responsibilities for a particular step in the process. Personnel can be support personnel, external partners, or suppliers.

   – *Machine/equipment.* In office processes these are computers, software system(s), and so on. In manufacturing processes these are machines, measuring equipment, and so on.

   – *Material/information.* In manufacturing processes, this is the raw material or component part. In transactional/business processes this can be information or a change notice, purchase order, invoice, or anything else being processed.

   – *Method/procedures.* Applicable policies, procedures, instructions, regulations, manuals, and so on.

   – *Measurement/QC checks.* Are you capturing any data at this step in your process? Are you performing a quality check here? How are the data being collected? Who is collecting the information? Are you using any measuring devices such as checklists or calipers, and so on, to collect the data?

   – *Environment or noise factors.* Are there any factors that you think might influence your process over which you have no control? For example, humidity, seasonal variation, operator absenteeism.

Repeat the brainstorming for each process step until all steps have inputs identified:

• *Categorize the inputs.* If your organization has already identified something as being critical, governed by a documented procedure, a requirement of a regulation, or a noise factor over which you have no control, you may want to also identify it through appropriate symbols, such as CR—critical, S—procedure, N—noise, C—control.

- *Identify the output for each step.* The output is known as the "*Y*"
  for a process step. One way to determine the output for each step
  is to ask the question, "How do I know that this step has been
  completed?" The answer to this question is the output for that
  particular step of the process. When documenting the output of the
  step, you need to also document what could go wrong in that step.
  Remember, don't play Chicken Little and say "the sky is falling";
  it is not your job to be paranoid. Be realistic and document only
  what could really go wrong. The desirable output of the step is
  a "positive (+) *Y*" and the undesirable output of the step is a
  "negative (–) *Y.*"

Determine the output for each process step until all steps have outputs
identified:

- Identify the output leaving the process (crossing the end point of
  your process). This is anything leaving the process and received
  by the customer.

- As before, you need to document both the desirable and
  undesirable output.

When you put all the information together in the form of a block diagram,
your process map is complete (see Figure 9). You are now ready to use
the second tool in the Measure phase, *failure mode and effects analysis*
(FMEA).

RISK MANAGEMENT PLAN FMEA

The process map must be completed before starting the FMEA. The FMEA
is a risk management tool that examines the process by looking at the failure modes, severity of effects, causes, and current inspection methodologies to evaluate where the risks lie. It assigns numbers 1 to 10 on a scale of
severity of the failure mode, frequency of occurrence, and current controls.
The resultant *risk priority number* (RPN) quantifies the risk for each step
in the process. The highest RPN number indicates the step in the process
with the maximum risk.

An FMEA is completed as follows based on the process map and input
from the process improvement team:

- *Step of the process.* Copy the first step of your process as shown in
  the process map in Figure 9.

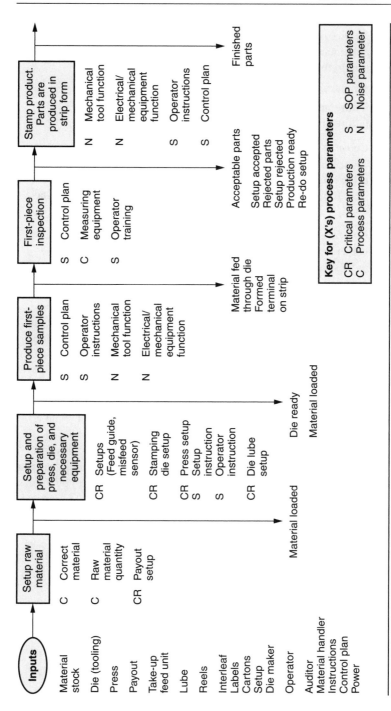

Figure 9 Example of a process map for a stamping process.

- *Failure mode.* The failure mode for the first step is what you had documented as the undesirable output or "negative (–) *Y*" for that step in the process map.

- *Failure effect.* Ask yourself the question, "What if this failure mode happens?" The answer to this question is the failure effect.

- *Cause.* Now ask the question, "What caused the failure mode to occur?" The answer is the cause. Look at the process map to see if the cause has been identified as one of the inputs (*X*'s) to that step. If not, add the cause to the process map. Note: you may have multiple causes for a single failure mode.

- *Controls.* List here the current inspection/check methodology. If there is no check being performed, state "None." Look at the process map; if there is an inspection methodology, make sure it is included as an input (*X*) for that step.

- Assign severity, occurrence, and detection numbers using a scale of 1 to 10. High numbers mean high severity, high occurrence, and poor detection capabilities. Low numbers mean low severity, low occurrence, and good detection.

- RPN (risk priority number) is the multiplication of severity # $\times$ occurrence # $\times$ detection #. A high RPN means high risk.

- For the high RPNs, the process improvement team must come up with action items to reduce those numbers. Use brainstorming methodology to come up with ideas. Recalculate new RPNs based on proposed action items. Note: The severity number can not change unless the step is redesigned. The new RPN must be lower than the initial RPN.

Repeat the above for every step in the process map until all steps are complete (see Figure 10).

Implement the ideas from the brainstorming session and identified action items.

Part/process	Failure mode	Failure effects	Sev	Causes	Occ	Controls	Det	RPN	Action recommended	Responsible person	Schedule date	Action taken	Actual completion date	PSO	POD	PRN
Setup raw material	Wrong raw material is received	Defective product, production slowdown, tool damage	7	Material not labeled correctly	2	Procedures are well defined	4	56	Current controls are effective							0
	Material is damaged or defective	Defective product, tool damage, equipment damage	7	Improper handling, poor incoming inspection	2	Licensed material handlers, material audited by receiving inspector	4	56	Current controls are effective							0
Setup and preparation of press, die, and necessary equipment	Press does not function properly	Can not run production	7	Controls not set up properly. Mechanical or electrical failure.	2	Proper training for setup personnel. PM program for equipment.	2	28	Current controls are effective							0
	Raw material does not feed into die properly	Can not run production, material jamming, damaged product, possible die damage.	8	Feed unit not functioning or set up properly. Material is out of spec. Payout not functioning properly. Die not set up properly.	2	Proper training for setup personnel. PM program for equipment.	4	64	Current controls are effective							0
	Improper die lubrication	Misformed product, excessive die wear, die damage.	7	Lube supply malfunction, lube supply not set up properly.	2	Proper training for setup personnel. Lube controllers.	4	56	Current controls are effective							0

Figure 10 Example of an FMEA.

Continued

Part/process	Failure mode	Failure effects	Sev	Causes	Occ	Controls	Det	RPN	Action recommended	Responsible person	Schedule date	Action taken	Actual completion date	PS	POD	PRPN
Produce first-piece samples	Parts not stamped correctly	Defective product.	8	Die not set up properly. Tooling worn or damaged.	2	Proper training for die technicians. PM program for tooling.	4	64	Current controls are effective							0
First-piece inspection	Operator does not perform first-piece inspection	Possible defective product produced. Terminal not capable of meeting customer requirements.	8	Operator lacking time. Poor training.	2	Procedures are well defined. Specified on control plan.	4	64	Current controls are effective							0
	Operator performs first-piece inspection incorrectly	Possible defective product produced. Terminal not capable of meeting customer requirements.	8	Lack of training. Incorrect use of gages and equipment.	2	Procedures are well defined. Specified on control plan.	4	64	Current controls are effective							0

Figure 10 *Continued.*

Part/process	Failure mode	Failure effects	Sev	Causes	Occ	Controls	Det	RPN	Action recommended	Responsible person	Schedule date	Action taken	Actual completion date	PS	PPO	PPD	PRPN
Stamp product. Parts are produced in strip form. Die stations: 0, 1 Date, gage, and ID stamps.	Stamps or anvils worn, broken, or missing. Wrong stamps.	No stamp, difficult to read, possible fracture of product and possible die damage. Traceability aspects impaired. Terminals misidentified.	8	Debris trapped in stamps. Stamps and/or anvil worn, broken, or missing. Improper heat treat, metal fatigue, and improper die setup.	2	Visual inspection by die makers, die setup personnel, operators, and floor auditors. Die setup procedures are well defined.	4	64	Current controls are effective								0
Stamping–die Die stations: 2–3, 3, 4, 6–7, 9–10, 11–12, 27, 42–43 Pierce, notch, and trim.	Pierce and/or trim punches or die blocks worn, missing, or broken	No pierce or trim. Possible misfeed. Excessive burrs, missing holes, irregular cuts. Improper forming in downstream forming stations. Possible die damage and out-of-spec parts.	8	Excessively worn tooling, metal fatigue, and improper heat treat. Lack of lubrication and improper die setup.	2	Visual inspection by die makers, die setup personnel, operators, and floor auditors. All heat treated tooling is checked using the Rockwell tester. Die setup procedures are well defined	4	64	Current controls are effective								0

Figure 10 *Continued.*

CALCULATING PROCESS SIGMA FOR YOUR PROCESS— PROCESS CAPABILITY

It is important for you to know how many defects are being made in your process (current state). The tool that is used to quantify defects or failure to meet customer requirements is known as process sigma. The *process sigma* denotes whether or not our process is capable of meeting customer specifications.

Before we start calculating process sigma, we must first understand some basics:

- Data collected through inspection can fall into one of the two data types: variable data or discrete data. *Discrete data* can be either attribute data or count data.

- *Variable data*, also known as continuous data, are collected where you use an instrument to measure and obtain a reading such as height, weight, density, thickness, force, length, and so on.

- *Attribute data* are commonly used to denote decisions such as pass/fail, accept/reject, go/no-go, good/bad, and so on.

- *Count data* denote the number of defects found in one unit, also known as defects per unit, or DPU. Examples: number of errors on an invoice, number of mistakes in a document, number of blemishes on a product, number of errors in a shipment, and so on.

The raw data collected through your inspection/QC check process need to be summarized if you are to obtain any useful information (see Figure 11). Data are summarized by calculating:

- The measure of central tendency, which indicates where the data are centered. The most common measure is the arithmetic average or *mean*.

- The measure of dispersion, which indicates the spread of the data. The most common measure is the *standard deviation*. The square of the standard deviation is called the *variance*.

A picture is worth a thousand words, and a bar chart/histogram may be used to graph the data and fit a curve over the histogram. The curve produced usually looks bell shaped.

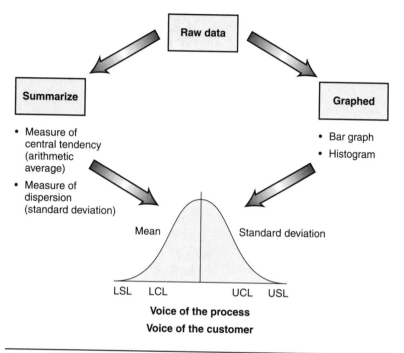

Figure 11 Summarizing raw data.

Fortunately, we can rely on any statistical software program to graphically summarize our raw data and put it all together with the mean and standard deviation values, providing us with information for interpretation and analysis:

- The upper control limit (UCL) and lower control limit (LCL) of the process can be calculated using the formulas "mean + 3 × standard deviation" and "mean – 3 × standard deviation." These values represent the voice of the process (VOP), since 99.73 percent of the data that were collected fall within the upper and lower control limits.

- The upper specification limit (USL) and lower specification limit (LSL) represent the voice of the customer (VOC). Ideally, if your process is to operate with no defects, then the VOP must be narrower than the VOC.

EXAMPLE 1

Cycle time data for obtaining approvals on deviations/waivers were collected for the past one year. Management stated that a deviation/waiver needed to be approved within three to seven business days of it being submitted for approval. What are the VOP and the VOC?

Stat > Basic Stat > Graphical Summary

In this example the process mean (average) is 5.2757 days and standard deviation is 0.2433 days (see Figure 12).

Voice of the Process

Lower control limit (LCL) = mean − 3 × standard deviation
= 5.2757 − (3 × .2433) = 4.5458 days

Upper control limit (UCL) = mean + 3 × standard deviation
= 5.2757 + (3 × .2433) = 6.0056 days

Voice of the Customer

Lower specification limit (LSL) = 3 days

Upper specification limit (USL) = 7 days

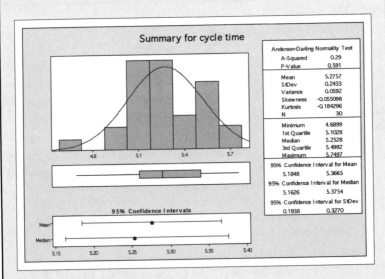

Figure 12 Histogram for cycle time.

CALCULATING PROCESS SIGMA (Z) OR PROCESS CAPABILITY (C$_p$ AND C$_{pk}$) FOR VARIABLE DATA

What are C_p and C_{pk}? The concept can be understood through the following analogy. Think of your process as the vehicle you are driving and the customer specification as the road on which you are driving. A $C_p = 1$ value means that the vehicle that you are driving is the size of a big truck and is the same width as the width of the road. A $C_p = 0.5$ value means that the vehicle that you are driving is oversized and is twice as wide as the road. Conversely, a $C_p = 2$ means that the vehicle that you are driving is a small car that is half the width of the road. Therefore, C_p is a comparison between the width of the customer specification (upper specification limit – lower specification limit) divided by the width of your process (6σ). Therefore $C_p = (USL - LSL) \div 6\sigma$.

C_p only tells us the size of the vehicle (whether the vehicle that we are driving is a car or a truck) but does not provide us with any information about our driving ability. A person is considered a good driver if the nose of their vehicle is always in the center of the road and there is an equal amount of space on either side of the road. If the vehicle is not centered, there is a tendency to be too close to one side or straddling lanes and causing an accident.

C_{pk} is a measure that describes our driving ability, or the ability of our process to meet specifications. In this example, if the center or average value of our process is the same as the target value of our specification, then our process is considered centered:

- A C_{pk} of 1 means that our process is centered on the target value of the specification and the width of the vehicle we drive is equal to the width of the road. In this scenario, there is no room for error. We must be always at the center of the road to avoid accidents (defects).

- A C_{pk} of 1.33 means that the vehicle is in the center of the road and there is a clearance of one standard deviation on either side. In this scenario, we have some room to move on the road without causing an accident.

- A C_{pk} of 2 means your vehicle is small and there is plenty of room to maneuver. Therefore, C_{pk} looks at the worst-case scenario by comparing half the width of the customer specification (upper specification limit – mean) or (mean – lower specification limit) divided by half the width of your process (3σ). Therefore, $C_{pk} = (USL - X\text{-bar}) \div 3\sigma$ or $(X\text{-bar} - LSL) \div 3\sigma$, whichever value is smaller. (Note: X-bar = arithmetic average, or the mean, and σ = standard deviation.)

The method for calculating process sigma for variable data is given in Table 1.

Table 1 Calculating process sigma—variable data.

Variable data (process sigma—*Z*)	Variable data C_p/C_{pk}
1. Collect data about the CTQ characteristic for your process.	1. Collect data about the CTQ characteristic for your process.
2. Calculate the average (mean) and standard deviation (σ) for your data.	2. Calculate the average (mean) and standard deviation (σ) for your data.
3. Determine the specification for your CTQ characteristic.	3. Determine the specification for your CTQ characteristic.
4. Process sigma is the number of times the process standard deviation (*s*) can be divided into the distance between the process center and the closest specification limit.	4. $C_p = (USL - LSL) \div 6\sigma$
5. Process sigma (*Z*) = (closest specification limit – process center) ÷ standard deviation	5. $C_{pk} = (USL - X\text{-bar}) \div 3\sigma$ or $(X\text{-bar} - LSL) \div 3\sigma$, whichever value is smaller.
6. Process sigma for variable data is considered short-term since we can quickly obtain data in a relatively short time.	6. Plug in the values of the specification limits and your process standard deviation to obtain C_p and C_{pk} values.
7. Convert short-term (ST) process sigma to long-term (LT) process sigma	*C_p and C_{pk} calculations for Example 1:*
8. Process sigma $_{ST}$ – 1.5 = Process sigma $_{LT}$	USL = 120 minutes
Example:	LSL = zero minutes (it doesn't matter how fast a user completes a task, but it does matter if a user takes too long)
Your company has captured task times of users performing software testing. You have sampled a set of 10 users; the summarized results are:	Mean (*X*-bar) = 104 minutes
	Standard deviation = 12 minutes
	$C_p = (USL - LSL) \div 6\sigma = (120 - 0) \div (6 \times 12) = 120 \div 72 = 1.67$.
	Therefore, $C_p = 1.67$. $C_{pk} = (USL - X\text{-bar}) \div 3\sigma$ or $(X\text{-bar} - LSL) \div 3\sigma$, whichever value is smaller.

Continued

Table 1 *Continued.*

Variable data (process sigma—Z)	Variable data C_p/C_{pk}
Mean: 104 minutes Standard deviation: 12 minutes USL: 120 minutes, LSL = 0 (it doesn't matter how fast a user completes a task, but it does matter if a user takes too long). Process sigma (Z) = (120 − 104) ÷ 12 (Z) = (16) ÷ 12 = 1.333	C_{pk} = (120 − 104) ÷ (3 × 12) = 120 ÷ 36 = 3.33. *or* C_{pk} = (104 − 0) ÷ (3 × 12) = 104 ÷ 36 = 2.89. Therefore, C_{pk} = 2.89 since the value 2.89 is smaller than 3.33. The answer for the software testing process is C_p = 1.67 and C_{pk} = 2.89.
Therefore, process sigma of 1.333 in the above example is process sigma (Z)$_{ST}$ = 1.333. For the software testing process, substituting in the above formulas we get: Process sigma $_{ST}$ − 1.5 = Process sigma $_{LT}$ (Z)$_{LT}$ = 1.333 − 1.5 = −0.166 Answer: The process sigma for the software testing process is (Z)$_{ST}$ = 1.333.	*Using Minitab to calculate process sigma (Z), C_p, and C_{pk}:* 1. Collect data about the CTQ characteristic for your process. 2. Enter it in Minitab in one column. 3. Minitab command: Stat > Quality Tools > Capability Analysis > Normal 4. At dialog box select the column of data and subgroup size. Note: Industry normally uses a subgroup size of four or five. What this means is that at every inspection period, you took a small sample of four or five pieces and measured each piece and documented the data. 5. Enter the upper and lower spec limit values. 6. In the Options tab > enter Target spec (if you have one); choose Percents and Capability Stats or PPM and Benchmark Z. Answer: Capability stats = C_p, C_{pk}, and Benchmark Z = Process sigma Z (Z.Bench). If you chose Percents, the graph will indicate percentage of your product not meeting specifications. If you chose PPM, the graph will indicate how many parts per million will not meet specification.

EXAMPLE 2

Length of a terminal is a critical customer dimension. 100 terminals were measured to determine if the process is capable of meeting specifications. Customer specification for terminal length is 2.250 to 2.270 cm, and target length is 2.260 cm (see Figure 13).

From the graph in Figure 14 the C_p value is 2.19, C_{pk} value is 1.87, and process sigma (Z.Bench) value is 5.62. The process average is slightly above the target value of 2.260 cm. All of the parts meet specification as seen under Exp. Overall Performance % Total (out of specification) = 0.00% or PPM (parts per million out of specification) = 0.18.

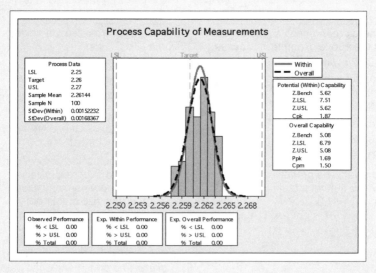

Figure 13   Process capability for terminal length showing percentage overall performance.

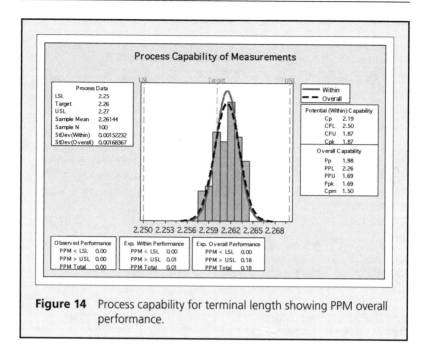

Figure 14   Process capability for terminal length showing PPM overall performance.

Calculating Process Sigma for Attribute and Count Data

The methods for calculating process sigma for attribute data and count data are given in Table 2.

Table 2   Calculating process sigma—attribute and count data.

Attribute data	Count data
Calculate rolled throughput yield (RTY):	*Calculate the total defects per lot of units checked:*
First-pass yield (FPY) can be calculated for each step of the process. If a process has three steps and FPY_1 is yield for step 1, FPY_2 is yield for step 2, FPY_3 is yield for step 3, then $RTY = FPY_1 \times FPY_2 \times FPY_3$.	Practical example: say we had checked a lot of 1200 quotations for errors, counted the total number of errors in the lot, and found the total errors to be 23.

Continued

Table 2   *Continued.*

Attribute data	Count data
Practical example: a purchase order process has three steps:	*Convert the figure into an average defects per unit, or average DPU:*
1. Receive a purchase requisition and check for accuracy—yield 98%	Average DPU for the above example = 23 ÷ 1200 = .01916
2. Create purchase order and check for accuracy—yield 97%	Use the formula Yield = e^{-DPU}:
	Substituting .01916 in the formula and solving (use calculator):
3. Verify and approve purchase order—yield 99%	Yield = $e^{-.01916}$ = .981022
RTY = $FPY_1 \times FPY_2 \times FPY_3$	This denotes that out of every 1000 quotations processed, 981 quotations will be free of errors.
RTY = $0.98 \times 0.97 \times 0.99 = 0.9411$	
This denotes that out of every 1000 purchase orders processed, 941 P.O.s will go through the process without any rework.	
Use Minitab or the standard normal distribution tables in Excel to arrive at the process sigma for the process:	*Use Minitab or the standard normal distribution tables in Excel to arrive at the process sigma for the process:*
Excel formulas:	Excel formulas:
=NORMSINV(0.9411)	=NORMSINV(0.981022)
Process sigma value (Z) = 1.564	Process sigma value (Z) = 2.075
Minitab command: Calc > Probability Distribution > Normal	Minitab command: Calc > Probability Distribution > Normal
At dialog box—choose Inverse Cumulative Probability and enter .9411 at Input Constant.	At dialog box—choose Inverse Cumulative Probability and enter .981022 at Input Constant.
Process sigma (Z) = 1.564	Process sigma (Z) = 2.075

Continued

Table 2 *Continued.*

Attribute data	Count data
Process sigma for attribute data is considered long-term since we require a large number of data points to calculate yield.	*Process sigma for count data is considered long-term since we require a large number of data points to calculate yield.*
Therefore, process sigma of 1.564 in the above example is	Therefore, process sigma of 2.075 in the above example is
Process sigma $(Z)_{LT}$ = 1.564.	Process sigma $(Z)_{LT}$ = 2.075.
Convert long-term (LT) process sigma to short-term (ST) process sigma:	*Convert long-term (LT) process sigma to short-term (ST) process sigma:*
Process sigma$_{ST}$ – 1.5 = Process sigma$_{LT}$	Process sigma$_{ST}$ – 1.5 = Process sigma$_{LT}$
where 1.5 is an empirical figure denoting process shift/ deterioration from short-term to long-term.	where 1.5 is an empirical figure denoting process shift/deterioration from short-term.
For the P.O. process, substituting in the above formulas we get:	For the quotation process, substituting in the above formulas we get:
Process sigma $(Z)_{ST}$ = 1.564 + 1.5 = 3.064	Process sigma $(Z)_{ST}$ = 2.075 + 1.5 = 3.575
Answer: the process sigma for the P.O. process is $(Z)_{ST}$ = 3.064.	Answer: the process sigma for the quotation process is $(Z)_{ST}$ = 3.575.

CONDUCTING GAGE R&R STUDIES—VARIABLE DATA AND ATTRIBUTE DATA

Gage repeatability and reproducibility (Gage R&R) is an analysis of the way you are currently capturing data about your process. This is also known as measurement systems analysis (MSA). The goal of conducting an MSA is to understand if one of the sources of variation is coming from the way you collect data. An ideal MSA will have data that are both repeatable and reproducible. Again, depending on the type of data that are collected we use different techniques for analyzing variable data and discrete data.

Conducting a Gage R&R for Variable Data

- Select 10 parts or items for which you want to measure a particular characteristic of interest.

- Parts must represent the range of specification, including parts within specification limits and outside specification limits.

- Select three operators. These are persons who normally measure the parts.

- Select the measuring instrument that you normally use to collect data, for example, caliper, micrometer, stopwatch, weighing scale. Be sure that the instrument is calibrated.

- Each part is measured by each operator in random order using the same measuring instrument. That is, 10 parts × 3 operators measuring each part once = 30 readings.

- This operation is repeated two more times.

- At the completion of the experiment, you must have 90 readings total. That is, 10 parts × 3 operators × 3 readings per part = 90 readings. You have thus run a total of three trials.

- Enter the data into your software program. Analyze the output from the software program.

- Acceptable values for a gage R&R for variable data are:

  – Gage R&R is less than 10 percent.

  – Part-to-part variation is greater than 90 percent.

  – Number of distinct categories is greater than or equal to five.

EXAMPLE 3
VARIABLE DATA GAGE R&R IN MINITAB
AND INTERPRETATION

Stat> Quality Tools> Gage Study> Gage R&R
Crossed – Xbar-R

A food processing company requires that a certain number of finished products be retained in inventory for testing purposes in case of consumer complaints. A test was conducted to ensure that all the food

---

technologists identified the correct number of samples to be retained in inventory for future testing purposes. An expert was also asked to recommend the correct number of samples to be retained. The gage R&R was conducted as follows:

- Ten situations were tested. Situations were randomly selected from historical scenarios.

- The test was given to one expert and three persons (total four persons).

- Three persons were randomly selected from a group of people who normally recommend the amount of products required to be retained.

- Each person was asked to repeat the test two more times.

- The amount of products required to be retained in inventory for testing was captured on the inventory request form.

- Data were tabulated and analyzed using Minitab (see Figure 15).

- *Components of Variation.* Gage R&R is not acceptable. It is 23.81 percent where it should be less than 10 percent. While repeatability is good (operators are consistent with themselves), operators are not consistent with others and the expert.

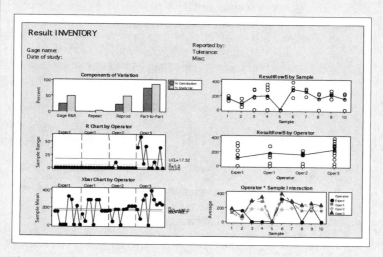

Figure 15   Gage R&R graph for inventory retained.

- *Range (R) Chart.* The range chart measures consistency across trials. Each situation was evaluated three times. If the food technologist provided the same answer across all three tries, then range = 0, meaning they were consistent, that is, repeatable. From the range chart you can tell that operator 3 is not consistent with himself and provided different requirements for the two trials. However, the expert, operator 1, and operator 2 were consistent during each of the three trials in stating the amount of samples that must be retained in inventory. Important note: Consistency here does not denote that they were consistent with the expert, only that they were consistent with their own figures. In order to evaluate whether the operators were consistent with the expert, we would have to look at the next chart which is "Xbar Chart by Operator."

- *X-bar Chart.* The overall pattern of the data (connected dots) should be a mirror image of that of the expert if the quantities reported are the same as the expert. In the *X*-bar chart, operators 2 and 3 have a different pattern than the expert. This means that they are not able to reproduce the data reported by the expert (they are inconsistent with the expert).

- *Result by Sample.* This graph represents the sample on the *x*-axis. This graph is a dot plot showing all four persons' values (three operators and one expert) for an individual situation. Each situation was evaluated three times by four persons (4 × 3 = 12). Therefore, the dots on the graph represent 12 readings for each situation. If the dots show minimal spread, it means there is not much of a difference. Looking at this graph, we can conclude that situation #4 had a lot of variation (each technologist reporting different requirements) while situation #1 had a small variation (close agreement on amount to be retained).

- *Result by Operator.* The *x*-axis denotes the amounts reported by each individual. We had 10 situations, each situation reviewed three times, giving a total of 30 readings. The black dot represents the grand average for that technician. If everyone is in agreement for all samples, then the grand averages should be the same. If they are the same, then the line connecting the grand averages should be a straight line. From the graph, operator 3 requires a higher average number of products to be retained in inventory compared with the others.

- *Operator * Sample Interaction.* For five of the 10 situations, based on tests administered by three persons, some operators are recommending that the company keep less inventory than what is required by the expert. Could this pose a risk to the company if insufficient amount of product is retained in inventory for testing?

EXAMPLE 4
GAGE R&R IN MINITAB AND INTERPRETATION

An electronics parts manufacturer wanted to know if the deflection of a particular part was being measured correctly by three different operators working on three shifts. Ten random samples were selected, both good and bad, and the deflection measured (see Figure 16). Results of the test are shown in Figure 17.

From these session window results from Minitab, we can conclude that this is a good gage since the "Total Gage R&R" is 3.06 percent. A good gage has a total R&R value of less than 10 percent. Repeatability

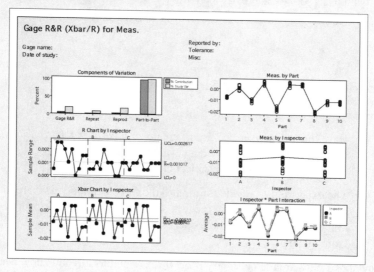

Figure 16   Minitab output for deflection measurement of electronic parts.

```
Gage R&R Study - XBar/R Method

                                    %Contribution
Source                 VarComp      (of VarComp)
Total Gage R&R         0.0000021         3.06
  Repeatability        0.0000004         0.53
  Reproducibility      0.0000017         2.52
Part-To-Part           0.0000654        96.94
Total Variation        0.0000675       100.00

                                  Study Var   %Study Var
Source                 StdDev (SD)  (6 * SD)     (%SV)
Total Gage R&R         0.0014359   0.0086154     17.48
  Repeatability        0.0006005   0.0036031      7.31
  Reproducibility      0.0013043   0.0078258     15.88
Part-To-Part           0.0080887   0.0485325     98.46
Total Variation        0.0082152   0.0492913    100.00

Number of Distinct Categories = 7
```

Figure 17   Results of deflection measurement of electronic parts.

and reproducibility are further broken down to 0.53 percent and 2.52 percent, indicating that there is more variation in reproducibility than in repeatability. The number of distinct categories reported is seven; we need this figure to be greater than five.

Conducting a Gage R&R for Discrete Data

Some activities to be done before actually conducting the test:

- Have the product/service expert create an *operational definition* for the product or service being evaluated. An operational definition states the accept/reject criteria.

- The expert must provide training to the three operators who are actually going to perform the test. The training must be provided at the same time so all three operators hear the same message from the expert.

The above steps are not necessary if the three operators already know what to do.

Running the test:

- Select 30 items for which you want to assess a particular characteristic of interest. Note: "item" here can represent either a product or service.

- Items must represent the range of criteria, both acceptable and unacceptable.

- Select three operators. These are persons who normally determine if the item is either acceptable or unacceptable.

- Select one person who is the expert on the criteria. This person represents the "gold standard" of the organization and is the last word on whether the product or service is acceptable or unacceptable.

- Each item is judged to be acceptable or unacceptable by each operator in random order using the same measuring instrument. That is, 30 parts × 3 operators measuring each part once = 90 readings.

- This procedure is repeated two more times.

- At the completion of the experiment, you must have 270 readings total, that is, 30 parts × 3 operators × 3 readings per part = 270 readings.

- Each item is judged to be acceptable or unacceptable by the expert once. Copy the expert's decision on each item two more times. Note: The rationale for copying the expert's judgment for each item is that the expert is always consistent. We are trying to quantify the inconsistency of the individual operators.

- Enter the data into your software program. Analyze the output from the software program.

- Acceptable values for a gage R&R for attribute data are:

  - Gage R&R: kappa value for operator versus expert is greater than 0.7.

  - Ideal kappa value = 1.

  - A kappa value of less than or equal to 0.7 indicates the need for training.

EXAMPLE 5
DISCRETE DATA GAGE R&R IN MINITAB
AND INTERPRETATION

Stat> Quality Tools> Attribute Agreement Analysis

Loan applications are processed by a bank using defined pass/fail criteria. Thirty applications were given to three appraisers in random order and they were asked to document their results as "pass" or "fail." A "pass" meant that the applicant received the loan, and a "fail" meant that the applicant was denied the loan. The 30 applications were also reviewed by an expert in the bank and his pass/fail decision documented. This information was entered into Minitab and comparisons made to determine the consistency of each appraiser and whether the appraiser's decision matched that of the expert (see Figure 18).

From the information given, we can conclude that while the three appraisers are consistent with their own decisions as to whether

Attribute Agreement Analysis for Rating
Within Appraisers

```
Assessment Agreement
Appraiser  # Inspected  # Matched  Percent          95 % CI
Boney            10          10     100.00  (74.11, 100.00)
Boris            10          10     100.00  (74.11, 100.00)
Roberto          10          10     100.00  (74.11, 100.00)

# Matched: Appraiser agrees with him/herself across trials.
```

Fleiss' Kappa Statistics

```
Appraiser  Response  Kappa  SE Kappa          Z  P(vs > 0)
Boney           f       1   0.182574  5.47723     0.0000
                p       1   0.182574  5.47723     0.0000
Boris           f       1   0.182574  5.47723     0.0000
                p       1   0.182574  5.47723     0.0000
Roberto         f       1   0.182574  5.47723     0.0000
                p       1   0.182574  5.47723     0.0000
```

Each Appraiser vs Standard
Assessment Agreement

```
Appraiser  # Inspected  # Matched  Percent         95 % CI
Boney            10           9     90.00  (55.50, 99.75)
Boris            10           9     90.00  (55.50, 99.75)
Roberto          10           9     90.00  (55.50, 99.75)
```

Figure 18   Appraiser results for bank loan pass/fail study.

Fleiss' Kappa Statistics

Appraiser	Response	Kappa	SE Kappa	Z	P(vs > 0)
Boney	f	0.607843	0.182574	3.32929	0.0004
	p	0.607843	0.182574	3.32929	0.0004
Boris	f	0.607843	0.182574	3.32929	0.0004
	p	0.607843	0.182574	3.32929	0.0004
Roberto	f	0.607843	0.182574	3.32929	0.0004
	p	0.607843	0.182574	3.32929	0.0004

Figure 18   *Continued.*

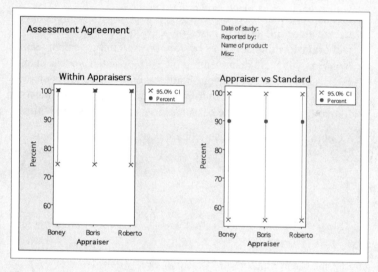

Figure 19   Attribute agreement analysis of bank loan gage R&R study.

to pass or fail a loan application, they do not agree with the expert's opinion. While their individual kappa value is 1 as seen in the "Within Appraisers" section, when each appraiser is compared with the standard or expert their Kappa value drops to 0.607843, suggesting the need for retraining.

The graph on the left in Figure 19 shows how consistent each appraiser was with their decisions when they reviewed the applications. The black dot on the graph is at 100 percent, and the vertical line indicates the 95 percent confidence interval for each appraiser. However, when we look at the graph on the right, we see that each of the appraisers agrees with the expert only 90 percent of the time.

END OF MEASURE PHASE

You have now reached the end of the Measure phase in the DMAIC process improvement methodology:

- Use the End of Measure Phase Checklist to ensure that all of the Measure phase activities have been completed.

- Collect objective evidence for items on the checklist and use them as a guide to present management with monthly updates.

- Follow good record keeping practice (whatever method works for your organization, electronic or hard copy).

- Create an action item list based on "current state" information and brainstorming activities by your process improvement team. Note: As you were documenting the current state (process map, FMEA, and gage R&R), you should have identified areas of your process that you would like to improve and suggestions you would like to try out. This is the basis for the Analyze phase activities.

- Celebrate the end of Measure phase activities with your team.

End of Measure Phase Checklist		
Items	**Place (✓) in box to indicate completion**	**Comments**
Process map current state or VSM		
FMEA		
Process capability • Variable data—C_p, C_{pk}, process sigma Z bench • Attribute data—process sigma Z_{ST} and Z_{LT} • Count data—process sigma Z_{ST} and Z_{LT}		
Gage R&R completed • Variable data (Gage R&R value, number of distinct categories) • Attribute data (kappa value)		
Summarized list of action items based on "current state" information and brainstorming activities by your process improvement team		
Communication plan being followed		
Meeting held with management • Roadblocks encountered		

III

Analyze

PURPOSE OF ANALYZE PHASE

The purpose of the Analyze phase is to help you better understand cause-and-effect relationships in your process, that is, which of the input factors exert an influence on the output, namely, the product or service you provide. At this phase of the process improvement methodology you are in essence filtering the large number of input factors and weeding out the insignificant ones by performing statistical analysis of the data collected.

The Analyze phase starts with implementing those action items that were identified by the process improvement team at the end of the Measure phase. Here you collect further data about your process after the changes are piloted. The data collected after the changes have been made is then subject to statistical analysis using any or all of these statistical tools:

- Hypothesis testing

- Correlation and regression

- Analysis of variance (ANOVA)

The use of the tools and interpretation of the statistical output are explained below. The interpretation helps you determine if a particular input factor to which you made changes has a significant influence on the output. If the result of your analysis shows "no significance," you know that you can, with confidence, disregard that input factor and proceed to run more tests until you have uncovered what is significant to your process.

ARE THINGS IMPROVING? RUNNING A HYPOTHESIS TEST

A *hypothesis* is an idea that is put forth and evaluated through testing of data. Results of the test allow you to conclude whether your idea was supported or disproved.

The logic behind hypothesis testing may sometimes appear backwards. In order to prove that an idea is supported, you must actually try to disprove that something really happened. However, if you *disprove* that nothing happened, you can come to the conclusion that something actually happened:

- "Nothing happened" is called the *null hypothesis*: H_0
- "Something happened" is called the *alternate hypothesis*: H_a

Conducting a Hypothesis Test

- Start out by writing the alternate hypothesis, H_a. It is easier for you to write this first. The alternate hypothesis is the answer to the question you want answered from the test. For example, if you would like to find out if the new software you installed has reduced invoice processing time, then the alternate hypothesis H_a is: *The average processing time taken by the new process is less than the average processing time taken by the old process.* This is statistically written as H_a: $\mu_{\text{New process}} < \mu_{\text{Old process}}$

- Next, write the null hypothesis, H_0. Since null means nothing, the null hypothesis is a state of "no change." It therefore becomes easy to write the null hypothesis since it is the opposite of the alternate hypothesis. Note that the "equal to (=)" sign always belongs in the null hypothesis. So for the example above, the null hypothesis is: *The average processing time taken by the new process is greater than or equal to the average processing time taken by the old process.* This is statistically written as H_a: $\mu_{\text{New process}} \geq \mu_{\text{Old process}}$

- State the alpha risk (α). The alpha risk is a guaranteed low probability of rejecting the null hypothesis wrongly. Stated otherwise, it is the level of confidence we have in our conclusion. This is also known as the level of significance. Industry normally sets the alpha risk at five percent; that is, the confidence is set at 95 percent. Table 3 gives some common alpha risk values.

Table 3   Common alpha risk values.

Confidence level	Alpha risk (α)	Probability (P) of alpha risk
95%	5%	.05
90%	10%	.10
99%	1%	.01

- Determine the number of sample data points, collect data, and run the appropriate test using any software package.

- Some general considerations about types of hypothesis tests:

  - Is it a one-tail or two-tail test? It is a one-tail test if the alternate hypothesis has a "greater than" or "less than" symbol.

  - Is it a *t*-test or a *Z*-test? It is a *t*-test if the sample size is less than or equal to 30 and the standard deviation is unknown. It is a *Z*-test when the sample size is greater than 30 and the standard deviation is known.

  - Is it a one-sample *t*-test or two-sample *t*-test? A one-sample *t*-test compares one column of data to a target or summarized historical value. It is a two-sample *t*-test when you are comparing two columns of data.

  - Is it a one-sample *Z*-test or two-sample *Z*-test?

  - Are we testing means or proportions? The *t*-test and *Z*-test are for testing means. Use proportion tests—one-proportion or two-proportion—when you have attribute data.

- Look at the results of the P value obtained after you have run the test. Based on the actual P value obtained, conclude whether to reject or fail to reject the null hypothesis at the stated alpha level of significance. One easy way to remember what to do is: if P value is low, H_0 must go! That is, if your calculated P value is less than your stated probability of alpha risk (0.05), then you must reject the null hypothesis H_0.

- Convert the statistical solution into a practical solution.

EXAMPLE 6

An engineer had designed a new tool. She wanted to find out if critical part dimensions made from two different cavities of the same tool were the same or different. If they are the same, the tool can be released to production.

Null hypothesis H_0: $\mu_{Cavity\ 1} = \mu_{Cavity\ 2}$

Alternate hypothesis H_a: $\mu_{Cavity\ 1} \neq \mu_{Cavity\ 2}$

Sample size = 252. The engineer had lots of data!

It was run as a two-sample *t*-test since the standard deviation was not known and she had two columns of data (see Figure 20). This is also a two-tail test; since the engineer is checking out "equal to" or "not equal to" she is interested in finding out if the cavities are the same. If the engineer wants to find out whether one cavity produces a larger or smaller part dimension, then it is a one-tail test.

Remember, if the calculated P value is less than your stated probability of alpha risk (0.05), then you must reject the null hypothesis H_0.

Answer

In this example the calculated P value is 0.118, which is greater than P value 0.05. Therefore, fail to reject the null hypothesis H_0.

$$\text{Stated null hypothesis } H_0: \mu_{\text{Cavity 1}} = \mu_{\text{Cavity 2}}$$

Therefore, the engineer concludes that cavity 1 is the same as cavity 2 (statistical solution).

Release tool to production (practical solution).

```
Cavity 1 vs. Cavity 2

all    N    Mean    StDev   SE Mean
  1   252  0.0067  0.0236   0.0015
  2   252  0.0033  0.0256   0.0016

Difference = mu (1) - mu (2)
Estimate for difference: 0.00343
95% CI for difference: (-0.00088, 0.00774)
T-Test of difference = 0 (vs not =): T-Value = 1.56
   P-Value = 0.118 DF = 498
```

Figure 20 Results of *t*-test of tooling cavity dimensions.

EXAMPLE 7

A pharmacy at a hospital was evaluated for the amount of time it took to fill each prescription. A new layout was proposed to decrease the amount of time. Data were captured on the time it took to fill seven prescriptions using the old layout and the proposed new layout. Management wants to know if the proposed new layout does indeed take less time to fill a prescription before committing to resources. What do you think?

Null hypothesis H_0: $\mu_{\text{New layout}} \geq \mu_{\text{Old layout}}$

Alternate hypothesis H_a: $\mu_{\text{New layout}} < \mu_{\text{Old layout}}$

Sample size = 7.

The hospital wants to pilot the proposal before committing resources to change the pharmacy layout.

The study is run as a two-sample *t*-test since the standard deviation is not known and there are two columns of data. This is also a one-tail test since the hospital is checking out whether "new layout time" is less than "old layout time." The patient does not have to wait as long if the time it takes to fill a prescription is lessened.

Results from Software: Stat> Basic Stat > Two sample T

Figure 21 shows the two-sample *t*-test for the new layout versus the old layout. From the box plot of the data, it appears that the new layout times have a slightly higher average but are more consistent (smaller standard deviation) when compared to the old layout times (relatively larger standard deviation).

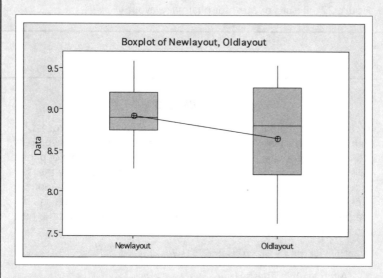

Figure 21   Output of *t*-test for pharmacy layout.

Remember, if the calculated P value is less than your stated proba-bility of alpha risk (0.05), then you must reject the null hypothesis H_0.

Answer

In this example the calculated P value is 0.814, which is greater than P value 0.05. Therefore, fail to reject the null hypothesis, H_0.

Stated null hypothesis, H_0 $\mu_{\text{New layout}} \geq \mu_{\text{Old layout}}$

Therefore, management concludes that the time taken to fill a prescrip-tion using the proposed new layout is the same or longer than with the old layout (statistical solution). Do not change stockroom layout (practi-cal solution).

```
              N    Mean   StDev   SE Mean
Newlayout    7    8.921   0.402      0.15
Oldlayout    7    8.649   0.655      0.25

Difference = mu (Newlayout) - mu (Oldlayout)
Estimate for difference: 0.272857
95% upper bound for difference: 0.805330
T-Test of difference = 0 (vs <): T-Value = 0.94
   P-Value = 0.814 DF = 9
```

Figure 22   Results of *t*-test for pharmacy layout.

EXAMPLE 8

A company document center recently came up with a new process for routing and obtaining approvals on documents. Since the new process was implemented, the document center has received a number of phone calls stating that document approval times have increased since the new process was implemented. The document center captured approval times (in hours) for 10 similar documents using the new process and the old process. Are the callers correct in their claim? That is, has the new process increased document approval time?

Null hypothesis H_0: $\mu_{\text{New process time}} \leq \mu_{\text{Old process time}}$

Alternate hypothesis H_a: $\mu_{\text{New process time}} \geq \mu_{\text{Old process time}}$

Sample size = 10.

The document center wants to determine whether the new processing time is indeed greater than the old processing time.

The study is run as a two-sample *t*-test since the standard deviation is not known and there are two columns of data. This is also a one-tail test since the document center is checking out whether "new processing time" is greater than "old processing time."

Results from Software: Stat> Basic Stat > Two sample T

From the box plot of the data (see Figure 23), it appears that the new process times have a higher average when compared to the old process times. However, there appears to be a greater variation within the old process approval times.

Remember, if the calculated P value is less than your stated probability of alpha risk (0.05), then you must reject the null hypothesis H_0.

Answer

In this example the calculated P value is 0.098, which is greater than P value 0.05 (see Figure 24). Therefore, fail to reject the null hypothesis H_0.

Stated null hypothesis H_0: $\mu_{\text{New process time}} \leq \mu_{\text{Old process time}}$

Therefore, the document center concludes that the time taken to approve a document using the new process is the same or less than with the old

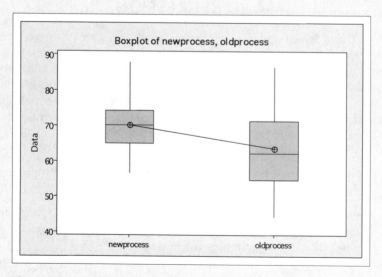

Figure 23 Output of *t*-test for document approval process.

process (statistical solution). The phone calls that the document center has been receiving about longer processing times are not substantiated (practical solution).

```
Two-Sample T-Test and CI: newprocess, oldprocess
Two-sample T for newprocess vs oldprocess

             N    Mean   StDev  SE Mean
newprocess  10   70.25    8.72     2.8
oldprocess  10   63.7     12.7     4.0

Difference = mu (newprocess) - mu (oldprocess)
Estimate for difference: 6.58009
95% lower bound for difference: -1.96270
T-Test of difference = 0 (vs >): T-Value = 1.35
   P-Value = 0.098 DF = 15
```

Figure 24 Results of *t*-test for document approval process.

CAN YOU UNCOVER ANY RELATIONSHIPS? CORRELATION AND REGRESSION

A tool used to determine if an input factor (X) and output factor (Y) are related is known as *correlation*. You can only run a correlation test when both the input (X) and the output (Y) are variable/continuous data. For example, the more hours you prepare for a test (X), the higher will be your grade (Y). Pearson correlation (r) is the most commonly used correlation coefficient, which quantifies the strength of a relationship between X and Y. The correlation coefficient (r) can only range from a value of +1 to –1:

- A value of $r = +1$ indicates 100 percent correlation; that is, all points fall on a line and the relationship between X and Y is positive (as the value of X increases, the value of Y increases).

- A value of $r = -1$ also indicates 100 percent correlation, but with an inverse relationship between X and Y (as the value of X increases, the value of Y decreases, or vice versa).

- A correlation coefficient of $r =$ zero means no relationship between X and Y exists.

How to run a correlation test:

- Write down the null and alternate hypotheses.

    - H_0: There is no correlation between X and Y

    - H_a: There is a correlation between X and Y

- Remember to compare the calculated probability (P value) against the probability of the alpha risk (P = 0.05).

    - If the calculated P value is less than 0.05, reject the null hypothesis and conclude in favor of H_a: that there is a correlation between X and Y.

    - If the calculated P value is greater than 0.05, fail to reject the null hypothesis and conclude in favor of H_0: that there is no correlation between X and Y.

- If the test concludes that there is a correlation between X and Y, then look at the Pearson correlation coefficient (r) value. This explains the strength and direction of the relationship.

EXAMPLE 9

A school wished to find out if there was a correlation between the number of students enrolled in a class and the number absent. The school captured enrollment data on 10 different classes and the number absent in each class over a one-month period.

Results from Software: Stat> Basic Stat > Correlation

Pearson correlation of number of students and number absent = 0.401

P value = 0.139

Answer

In this example the calculated P value is 0.139, which is greater than P value 0.05. Therefore, fail to reject the null hypothesis H_0.

Stated null hypothesis H_0: There is no correlation between X and Y

The school concludes that there is no relationship between the size of the class and the number of students absent.

Note: Since we have concluded that there is no correlation, we do not have to worry about the correlation coefficient (r).

EXAMPLE 10

A company wishes to know if there is any correlation between the time taken to create a purchase order and the number of items ordered. This data was collected by the purchasing department over a two-week period.

Results from Software: Stat> Basic Stat > Correlation

Pearson correlation of time to create P.O. and number of items ordered = 0.932

P value = 0.000

Answer

In this example the calculated P value is 0.000, which is less than P value 0.05. Therefore, reject the null hypothesis H_0. (If P value is low, H_0 must go.)

Alternate hypothesis H_a: There is a correlation between X and Y

The company concludes that there is a relationship between the number of items ordered and the time it takes to create a P.O.

Now look at the Pearson correlation (r) value; it is 0.932, which means that there is a strong positive relationship. That is, as more items are ordered, it takes longer to create a P.O.

Regression is a tool that helps us quantify the relationship between X and Y. You can proceed to do regression only if you have first passed the correlation test and established a relationship between X and Y. The input factor (X) is known as the *independent variable,* and the output factor (Y) is known as the *dependent variable,* or *response.* Regression is fitting a line or a curve to the data, and the equation of the line or curve is what is known as the *regression equation.* The regression equation, or *prediction equation,* can then be used to predict the value of the output Y by changing the value of the input X.

There are some important features in the output to look for:

- *P value.* A calculated low P value (when compared to alpha risk) indicates that the regression equation is significant.

- *Standard deviation (s).* Indicates how far the calculated value can differ from the true value.

- *R-sq (adjusted)*. Expressed in percentage; also known as the coefficient of determination. R-sq explains the amount of variation in *Y* attributable to *X*. For example, the greater number of hours you prepare for a test (*X*), the higher will be your grade (*Y*). If you get an R-sq (adjusted) value of, say, 49 percent, you can then claim that 49 percent of the higher grade in the test is directly attributable to the number of hours spent preparing for the test.

- Look at the graph of residuals. Residuals are what are remaining. These data must exhibit a random pattern (no bands, fan-shaped pattern, slopes, and so on).

EXAMPLE 11
CORRELATION AND REGRESSION IN MINITAB

An injection molding company wants to determine if there is a relationship between the density and breaking strength of a new type of plastic. Twenty products of different density were tested in the lab and breaking strength recorded.

Results from Software: Stat> Basic Stat > Correlation

Pearson correlation of density and strength = −0.861

P value = 0.000

Answer

In this example the calculated P value is 0.000, which is less than P value 0.05. Therefore, reject the null hypothesis H_0. (If P value is low, H_0 must go.)

Alternate hypothesis H_a: There is a correlation between *X* and *Y*

The company concludes that there is a relationship between density and strength.

Now look at the Pearson correlation (*r*) value; it is −0.861, which means that there is a strong negative or inverse relationship. That is, as density increases, strength decreases.

Since we have correlation, we can go to regression to determine the mathematical model for the relationship.

Results from Software: Stat > Regression > Regression

The regression equation is Strength = 116.0 − 335.1 Density

$$S = 4.53255, \text{R-sq} = 74.1\%, \text{R-sq (adj)} = 72.3\%$$

Analysis of Variance

```
Source        DF       SS       MS      F       P
Regression     1    824.80   824.803  40.15  0.000
Error         14    287.62    20.544
Total         15   1112.42
```

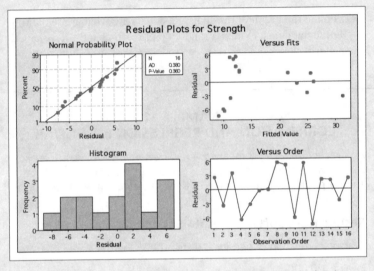

Figure 25 Output of correlation/regression test for plastic density versus strength.

Answer

In this example:

- The regression equation is Strength = 116.0 – 335.1 Density.

- P value = 0.000 indicates that the regression equation is significant.

- Standard deviation (s) = 4.53255 indicates how far the predicted value can differ from the true value when the regression equation is used.

- R-sq (adjusted) = 72.3% explains that 72.3 percent of the variation in strength is attributable to density.

- Look at the graph of residuals versus fits in Figure 25. Residuals are what are remaining. The residuals are normally distributed with no patterns.

ANOVA (ANALYSIS OF VARIANCE)

We are now bringing in the big guns of analysis to help us identify those input factors that are influential on our process. You have already been introduced to hypothesis testing. A simple hypothesis test asks the question in terms of a null hypothesis, essentially stating that everything is equal. If the null hypothesis is rejected, then we can say that "the difference is significant" ($P < 0.05$).

Simply put, ANOVA is hypothesis testing on steroids:

- The null hypothesis in ANOVA is: *All means are equal;*
  H_0: $\mu_1 = \mu_2 = \mu_3 = \mu_4 \ldots = \mu_n$

- The alternate hypothesis in ANOVA is: H_a: *At least one mean is different.* It does not tell us which one is different. We will have to run a further test to determine which one is different.

- The tests in ANOVA are based on the F ratio, which is the ratio of the variation between input factors to the variation within the factor. If the between-factor variation is substantially greater than the within-factor variation, then we can conclude that some factor or factor(s) are significant and reject the null hypothesis based on a predetermined P value such as 0.05.

- Remember, if P value is low, H_0 must go! That is, if the calculated P value is less than your stated probability of alpha risk (0.05), then you must reject the null hypothesis H_0 and rule in favor of the alternate hypothesis H_a: *at least one mean is different!*

One-Way ANOVA and Two-Way ANOVA

For the purposes of this book, we will limit ourselves to the explanation of one-way and two-way ANOVA. One-way ANOVA has only one input factor while two-way ANOVA has two input factors.

For example, if we wanted to find out the conditions that give us the maximum gas mileage for our car, we could set up an experiment to study the effect of different types of gasoline on mileage. We could run our experiment using name brand gas #1, name brand gas # 2, and generic brand gas #3. Our input factor is gasoline type. The output factor is the number of miles per gallon (mpg). This type of experiment is known as one-way ANOVA since we have only one input factor.

Suppose we were to set up the experiment differently, where we tested gasoline type and also tire pressure, and measured the mpg. This is known as a two-way ANOVA. We have two inputs in this example: gasoline type and tire pressure. Our output is the number of miles per gallon (mpg).

Steps for ANOVA

- Set up the experiment and determine the number of input factors.

- Choose the number of levels in each input factor. In the example above, gasoline type has three levels: name brand gas #1, name brand gas # 2, and generic brand gas #3.

- If you are doing a two-way ANOVA, choose the same number of levels for the second factor as you have for the first factor. Therefore, tire pressure has three levels: rated nominal pressure, high pressure, and low pressure.

- Determine your output: what are you going to measure (for example, mpg)?

- Conduct the test and collect the data.

- Use a software program to do the calculations.

- Perform a graphical analysis:

  - Look at main effects graph if conducting a one-way ANOVA.

  - Look at the main effects and interactions graphs if conducting a two-way ANOVA.

  - Use Minitab software commands Stat > ANOVA > Main Effects Plot and Stat > ANOVA > Interactions Plot.

- Test ANOVA assumptions (for factors):

  - Data are not correlated.

  - Data are normally distributed.

  - Variances are equal.

- Perform a statistical analysis. There are some important features in the output to look for:

  - *P value.* Indicates whether the factor is "significant" or "not significant." Remember: if calculated P value (when compared to alpha risk) is low, H_0 must go! Then you must reject the null hypothesis H_0 and rule in favor of the alternate hypothesis H_a: *At least one mean is different!*

- *R-sq (adjusted)*. Expressed in percentage; also known as the coefficient of determination. R-sq explains the amount of variation in *Y* attributable to *X*.

- Look at the graph of residuals. Residuals are what are remaining. These data must exhibit a random pattern (no bands, fan-shaped pattern, slopes, and so on).

• Follow up with a Tukey test if performing a one-way ANOVA and you get a calculated P value of < 0.05, indicating that at least one mean is different:

- *Interpretation of the output from a Tukey test.* The Tukey test subtracts confidence limits; therefore, if you find the value zero (0) contained within the span of readings, then there is no difference between the means. If zero (0) is not contained, that is, the span of readings are either all positive numbers or all negative numbers, then the means are different.

• A two-way ANOVA does not require a Tukey test. You can look at the factor and interaction P values to determine significance (significance = P < 0.05).

• Convert the statistical solution to a practical solution.

Cheat sheets for the ANOVA assumptions are shown in Table 4.

Table 4   Cheat sheets for ANOVA assumptions.

ANOVA	H$_0$ and H$_a$	P value compared to alpha risk (P = 0.05)	Software command
Assumption #1. Data are not correlated	H$_0$: Data are not correlated, that is, data are independent.	Calculated P value ≥ 0.05 indicates no correlation.	Stat > Basic Stat > Correlation
	H$_a$: Data are correlated, that is, data are dependent.	P value < 0.05 indicates correlation.	

Continued

Table 4 *Continued.*

ANOVA	H_0 and H_a	P value compared to alpha risk (P = 0.05)	Software command
Assumption #2. Data are normally distributed	H_0: Data are normal. H_a: Data are not normal.	Calculated P value ≥ 0.05 indicates that data are normal. P value < 0.05 indicates that data are not normal (skewed).	Stat > Basic Stat > Normality Test
Assumption #3. Variances are equal	H_0: Variances are equal. H_a: Variances are not equal.	Calculated P value ≥ 0.05 indicates that variances are equal. P value < 0.05 indicates that variances are not equal.	Stat > ANOVA > Test for Equal Variances
One-way ANOVA	H_0: All means are equal. H_a: The means are not equal (at least one is different).	Calculated P value < 0.05 indicates that at least one mean is different. Follow up with Tukey test to determine which mean is different.	Stat > ANOVA > One-Way. Tukey family error rate 5.
Two-way ANOVA	H_0: Means are equal; there is no interaction between factors. H_a: The means are not equal; there is an interaction between factors.	Calculated P value < 0.05 indicates which factor mean or interaction is significant.	Stat > ANOVA > Two-Way

Continued

Table 4 *Continued.*

Note: For ANOVA, input factors (*X*'s) may be a mixture of both variable data and/or categorical data. Output (*Y*) must be variable data. One-way or two-way ANOVA will not give us a mathematical model.

If both the input and output are variable data, then this special case of ANOVA is called regression. Regression will give us a mathematical model.

EXAMPLE 12
ONE-WAY ANOVA

A hospital administration wanted to determine if there were any differences in the ambulance response time at three hospitals. They took 10 random samples at each of the locations and measured the response time in minutes for the ambulance to arrive at the scene. This is a one-way ANOVA problem with hospital as the input factor and response time as the output. The input factor has three levels: hospital 1, hospital 2, and hospital 3.

Analyzing the Problem Using Software

- Perform a graphical analysis:

  - Look at main effects if conducting a one-way ANOVA.

  - Software command Stat > ANOVA > Main Effects Plot.

    o From the main effects plot (Figure 26), hospital 1 appears to be taking the least amount of time and hospital 3 taking the most.

- Test the three ANOVA assumptions (for factors) (Figure 27):

  - Data are not correlated. Stat > Basic Statistics > Correlation.

  - Data are normally distributed. Stat > Basic Statistics > Graphical Summary.

  - Variances are equal. Stat > ANOVA > Test for Equal Variances.

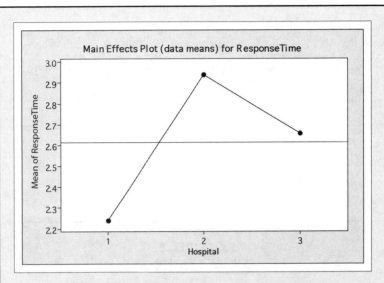

Figure 26   Main effects plot for ambulance response time.

Correlations: ResponseTime_1, ResponseTime_2, ResponseTime_3

```
                ResponseTime1  ResponseTime2
ResponseTime2        0.179
                     0.621

ResponseTime3       -0.099         0.256
                     0.785         0.475

Cell Contents: Pearson correlation

              P-Value
All p-values are high i.e. > 0.05; indicating data is not
correlated.
```

Figure 27   Results of ANOVA assumptions test for factors.

- The P values for the Anderson-Darling normality test for all three hospitals are high (see Figures 28, 29, and 30). Hospital 1 = 0.794, hospital 2 = 0.874, and hospital 3 = 0.812, indicating that the data are normally distributed.

- The Bartlett's test P value is high (P = 0.609), indicating that the variances are equal (see Figure 31). You can now conclude that all three ANOVA assumptions have been met.

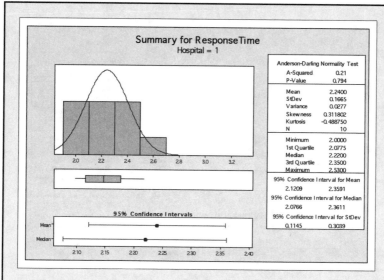

Figure 28 Anderson-Darling normality test for hospital 1.

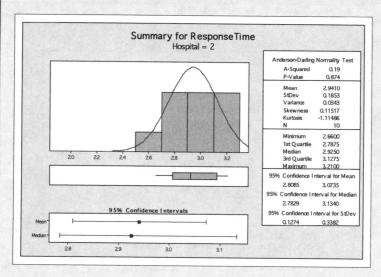

Figure 29 Anderson-Darling normality test for hospital 2.

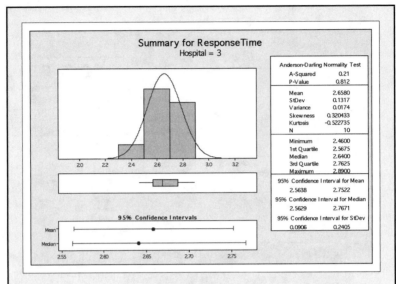

Figure 30   Anderson-Darling normality test for hospital 3.

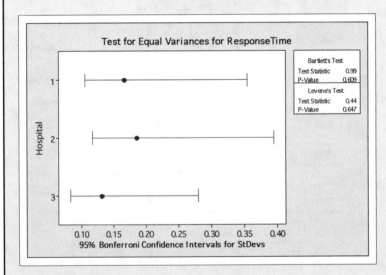

Figure 31   Bartlett's test for ambulance response times.

```
Source    DF    SS      MS      F      P
Hospital   2  2.4874  1.2437  47.00  0.000
Error     27  0.7144  0.0265
Total     29  3.2018

S = 0.1627 R-Sq = 77.69% R-Sq(adj) = 76.03%
P-value = 0.000, indicating hospital is significant, and that
   at least one hospital type has a different response time.
R-Sq(adj) = 76.03% indicating that 76.03% of the variation in
   response time is explained by the type of hospital.
```

Figure 32   Results of statistical analysis of ambulance response times.

- Perform a statistical analysis (see Figure 32). There are some important features in the output to look for:

  - *P value*. Software command: Stat > ANOVA > One Way. Indicates whether the factor is significant or not significant. Remember: If the calculated P value (when compared to alpha risk) is low, H_0 must go! Then you must reject the null hypothesis H_0 and rule in favor of the alternate hypothesis H_a: *At least one mean is different.*

  - *R-sq (adjusted)*. Expressed in percentage; also known as the coefficient of determination. R-sq explains the amount of variation in *Y* attributable to *X*.

  - Look at the graph of residuals versus the fitted values in Figure 33. Residuals are what are remaining. This data must be exhibited in a random pattern (no bands, fan shaped pattern, slopes, and so on).

- Residuals are normally distributed, with no obvious pattern.

- Since our P value = 0.000, we follow up with a Tukey test (Figure 34) to determine which of the hospitals has a significantly different response time.

When comparing hospital 1 to hospital 2, the subtracted confidence interval does not contain zero (0), indicating that the hospitals have different mean response times. Since the sign is positive, it indicates that the mean response time of hospital 2 is greater than the mean response time of hospital 1.

When comparing hospital 1 to hospital 3, the subtracted confidence interval does not contain zero (0), indicating that the hospitals have different mean response times. Since the sign is positive, it indicates that the mean response time of hospital 3 is greater than the mean response time of hospital 1.

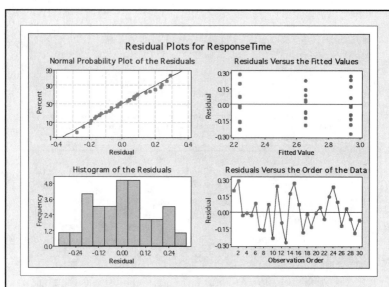

Figure 33   Output of residual plots for ambulance response times.

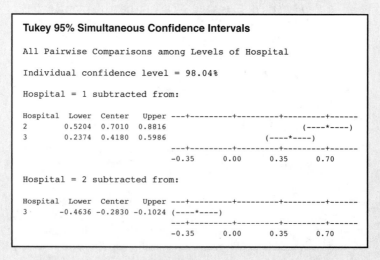

Figure 34   Tukey test results for ambulance response times.

When comparing hospital 2 to hospital 3, the subtracted confidence interval does not contain zero (0), indicating that the hospitals have different mean response times. Since the sign is negative, it indicates that the mean response time of hospital 3 is less than the mean response time of hospital 2.

Conclusion

The mean response times of all three hospitals are different. Hospital 1 takes the least amount of time while hospital 2 takes the most amount of time. However, only 76.03 percent of the response time is attributed to the location of the hospital. There is some other unexplained factor influencing the response time.

EXAMPLE 13
TWO-WAY ANOVA

The hospital administration collected more data on the ambulance service providers to determine whether service provider A or B had a different effect on the response time. This is a two-way ANOVA problem with hospital and service provider as the input factors and response time as the output.

Since we checked out the assumptions earlier under one-way ANOVA, we will go straight to the graphical and statistical analyses.

Stat > ANOVA > Main Effects Plot

The main effects plot (Figure 35) shows service provider A taking more time than service provider B.

Stat > ANOVA > Interactions Plot

The interactions plot (Figure 36) shows that there are no interactions between service provider and hospital.

Statistical Analysis: Stat > ANOVA > Two Way

The ANOVA table (Figure 37) shows both service provider and hospital as being significant, with low P values. However, interaction is not significant since the P value is high (P = 0.895). R-sq (adj) = 79.94 percent indicates that while both service provider and hospital are significant, there is still 20.06 percent of the variation not explained; there is some other unexplained factor causing the variation in response time.

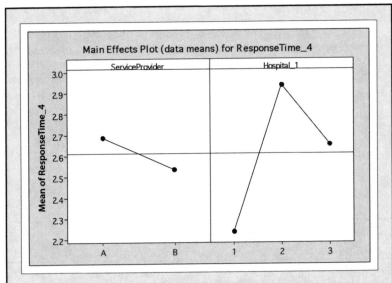

Figure 35 Main effects plot for two-way ANOVA of ambulance response times.

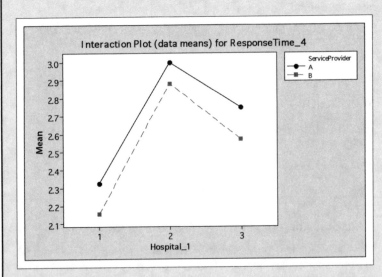

Figure 36 Interactions plot for two-way ANOVA of ambulance response times.

```
Two-way ANOVA: ResponseTime_4 versus ServiceProvider,
Hospital_1

Source          DF      SS       MS      F       P
ServiceProvider  1   0.17787  0.17787   8.03   0.009
Hospital_1       2   2.48738  1.24369  56.14   0.000
Interaction      2   0.00494  0.00247   0.11   0.895
Error           24   0.53164  0.02215
Total           29   3.20183

S = 0.1488 R-Sq = 83.40% R-Sq(adj) = 79.94%
```

Figure 37 ANOVA table for ambulance response times.

END OF ANALYZE PHASE

You have now reached the end of the Analyze phase in the DMAIC process improvement methodology:

- Use the End of Analyze Phase Checklist to ensure that all of the Analyze phase activities have been completed.

- Collect objective evidence for items on the checklist and use them as a guide to present management with monthly updates.

- Follow good record keeping practice (whatever method works for your organization, electronic or hard copy).

- Update your action item list that you created in the Measure phase with information from all the tests. Note: as you run these tests, you gain a greater knowledge as to what input factors are significant and what factors are not significant in your process.

Items	Place (✓) in box to indicate completion	Comments
End of Analyze Phase Checklist		
Hypothesis test • P value • Result: H_0 or H_a?		
Correlation • P value • Pearson *r* value • Result: H_0 or H_a?		
Regression • P value • Mathematical model • R-sq (adjusted) • Residuals OK?		
One-way ANOVA • P value • R-sq (adjusted) • Residuals OK? • Result: H_0 or H_a? • Follow-up Tukey test? • Result of Tukey (which means are different?) • Main effects plot		
Two-way ANOVA • P value for factors and interactions • R-sq (adjusted) • Residuals OK? • Which factor or interaction is significant? • Main effects plot • Interactions plot		
Communication plan being followed		
Meeting held with management • Roadblocks encountered		
Note: you may run multiple tests for each type, if results warrant.		

IV

Improve

PURPOSE OF IMPROVE PHASE

By the end of the Analyze phase, you have a gained a greater understanding of your process that you are trying to improve. Regression provides an insight into relationships, ANOVA identifies which of the input factors are significant, and hypothesis tests tell you if your hunch is correct or if you should be trying something else.

You are now ready to take all this knowledge and model your process in terms of inputs and output. A tool used in this stage is called design of experiments (DOE). The purpose of a DOE here, therefore, is to mathematically model your process with the significant input factors from the Analyze phase and come up with a relationship that will help you better control the behavior of the input factors.

INVESTIGATING RELATIONSHIPS BETWEEN INPUTS AND OUTPUT—RUNNING DESIGN OF EXPERIMENTS (DOE)

Activities associated with a DOE include the front end, that is, planning the experiment, as well as the statistical analysis. The mathematics behind the DOE are nothing but ANOVA. We already discussed ANOVA in the Analyze phase, and you will by now be familiar with identifying input factors that are significant or not significant by looking at their corresponding P value. Significance indicates that an input factor has an influence on the process (namely, it plays a critical role). However, the role played by a factor can be either favorable or unfavorable to the process. The thought process is as follows: if you know which of the factors are significant and their role in or contribution to the process, it becomes easy to control those factors in the future by specifying the limits or values they can take to assure that the process continues to meet requirements. Your job of process improvement will then be achieved!

67

While there are many types of DOE, the DMAIC process improvement methodology primarily limits itself to discussing characterization designs. *Characterization designs* are selected when you wish to model your process and obtain an equation to predict process performance. With the help of the prediction equation, you can now manipulate the input factor settings to ensure that your output consistently meets requirements. You are moving from passively inspecting your output to proactively ensuring compliance.

Steps for Conducting a DOE

- Planning steps:

  - *Define the output (Y).* The output (*Y*) is also called the response variable. What are you going to measure? How are you going to measure it? Have you established measurement definitions? What kind of instrument are you going to use to measure the data? Have you performed a gage R&R on the instrument? What is the value? Do you have a form or should a form be created for collecting data? Do you have a data collection plan?

  - *Finalize the input factors (X's).* The input factors are the variables that you will be controlling in the experiment. Input factors, when adjusted, have an effect (positive, negative, or minimal) on the output/response variable. What are the operator-controlled process variables? Are there any noise variables or classification factors such as shift, operator, supplier, and so on, that you would like to consider? If in doubt, refer to your process map; consider significant input factors identified in the Analyze phase.

  - *Set the values for each input factor.* The values are also known as levels for input factors. Are the levels qualitative or quantitative? The range of values (high and low settings) may be set from experience.

  - *Estimate time and cost.* When do you plan to run the experiment? How long will it take? Who will be involved? Are there any costs to be considered?

  - *Conduct a dry run to verify that all the settings of the input factors work and do not preclude other settings.* Check to make sure you are operating within safety limits if the experiment involves equipment.

  - *Finalize the input factors and levels.*

- *Conduct the experiment.* Don't forget to perform a gage R&R prior to running the experiment. Set up a spreadsheet, collect data, and tabulate per the software program that you use. Some tips for running the experiment:

  - Do not delegate the responsibility for running the experiment to the operators and testers; be present during the experiment to observe and take notes.

  - Preferably randomize the experimental runs in order to eliminate any bias; the computer program will do this for you. The run order on the computer-generated spreadsheet indicates the order in which the experiment should be run.

  - Ensure that you have everything ready for performing the experiment, such as equipment, measuring device, material, personnel, note pad, and so on.

  - Set the input variable values/levels (X's) for each run based on the run order from the spreadsheet. Measure the output/response (Y) of the process and record the result. Change the settings of the input variable for the next run, measure, and record the output. Proceed in this fashion until all the experimental runs are completed and data has been captured and recorded. The data are now ready to be analyzed.

- *Analyze the results using the software program.*

- *After analysis, verify new processing conditions using the mathematical model provided by the software after analysis.*

- *Make improvements permanent.* Convert the statistical solution into a practical solution.

Note: In some instances, the results of one experiment may suggest further experimentation. If so, plan for the next DOE, and repeat the steps outlined above.

Steps for DOE in Software

- *Set up the worksheet.* Use Stat > DOE > Factorial > Create Factorial Design > 2-Level Factorial Design. A two-level design means that each input factor selected has two levels; namely, it can be set at a low value and a high value. It is up to the experimenter to select the appropriate low and high values for each input factor.

- *Run the experiment, collect the data, and enter them into the software program.* Print out the worksheet and have the team follow the factor settings for each input factor on the spreadsheet in the run order that was created. Have one person on the team record the response (output) and take notes as the experiment progresses. These notes will be helpful later on during data analysis.

- *Review the graphical analyses.*

   - *Main effects plot.* Use Stat > ANOVA > Main Effects Plot.

   - *Interactions plot.* Use Stat > ANOVA > Interaction Plot.

   - Note: You can also use Stat > DOE > Factorial > Factorial Plots. This will give you the main effects plot, interactions plot, as well as a cube plot.

   - *Four-in-one graph of the residuals* (look for patterns already discussed in ANOVA).

- *Review the statistical analysis.* Use Stat > DOE > Factorial > Analyze Factorial Design.

   - *Compare P value to alpha risk.* When a calculated P value is less than the alpha risk, it indicates that the factor is significant.

   - Determine which factor is significant (initially set P value at 0.10 and confidence level at 90 percent).

   - Now drop the insignificant terms for the next round of analysis using the software (reset P value to 0.05 and confidence level to 95 percent).

   - Rerun analysis using software and compare the calculated P value to 0.05. Only those factors that have calculated P values that are less than 0.05 are significant. Be careful when dropping insignificant terms. The rule is: if a factor by itself is not significant but the interaction with another factor is significant, then you can not drop the main factor out of the analysis. Look at both the P value and R-sq (adjusted). Note: R-sq (adjusted) explains the amount of variation due to the influence of the selected factors on the response.

- *Obtain the prediction equation.* Use the response optimizer (Stat > DOE > Factorial > Response Optimizer).

EXAMPLE 14
DESIGN OF EXPERIMENTS—GLUTEN DISSOLUTION

A food processing manufacturer wanted to determine the important factors affecting dissolution time of a certain type of gluten. The input factors chosen for the study were:

Cook time (minutes)	Percent (%) concentration	Cook temperature (degrees)
2	5	400
3	10	450

Response (output) = Dissolution time in water, measured in seconds

This experiment was set up as a three-factor design, with each factor having two levels, or a low and high setting. The experimenter chooses to run the experiment with two replicates, namely, two experimental runs with the same factor settings (levels). For example, the factor-setting combination of cook time two minutes, concentration five percent, and cook temperature 400 degrees is replicated (see Table 5).

Table 5 Experimental worksheet and results—gluten dissolution experiment.

Cook time (minutes)	Percent (%) concentration	Cook temperature (degrees)	Dissolution time
2	5	400	15.36
3	5	400	7.64
2	10	400	15.60
3	10	400	3.66
2	5	450	28.20
3	5	450	22.80
2	10	450	26.06
3	10	450	17.82
2	5	400	16.88
3	5	400	3.8
2	10	400	16.70

Continued

Table 5 *Continued.*

Cook time (minutes)	Percent (%) concentration	Cook temperature (degrees)	Dissolution time
3	10	400	1.44
2	5	450	23.62
3	5	450	27.48
2	10	450	22.48
3	10	450	15.10

The experiment was conducted and dissolution time recorded for each combination of input factor settings. The data were analyzed using a software package.

- *Review the graphical analyses.*

    - *Main effects plot.* Use Stat > ANOVA > Main Effects Plot. The *y*-axis in Figure 38 represents dissolution time and the *x*-axis on each graph shows the low setting and high setting for each input factor. The two black dots within each graph represent the average dissolution time taken at the low and high settings for that input factor. Cook time and cook temperature apparently have a greater effect than concentration on dissolution time. Figure 38 tells us that when cook time is set low, it takes longer for the gluten to dissolve. However, when the cook temperature is set low, the gluten dissolves in less time. Figure 38 also tells us that there is not a large disparity in dissolution time when concentration levels are changed.

    - *Interactions plot.* Use Stat > ANOVA > Interaction Plot (Figure 39). There appears to be a slight interaction between concentration and cook time at the low setting and cook time and cook temperature at the high setting. However, we will look at the calculated P value obtained for the interaction terms when we do our statistical analysis to help us determine if the interactions are significant.

    - *Review the factorial plot.* Use Stat > DOE > Factorial > Factorial Plots. The cube plot (Figure 40) shows the relationship between the input factors and dissolution time. The figure at each corner is the average dissolution time for that combination of settings. For the dissolution time data,

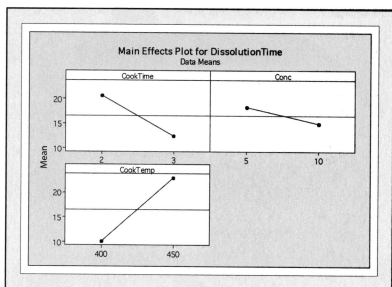

Figure 38 Main effects plot for gluten dissolution experiment.

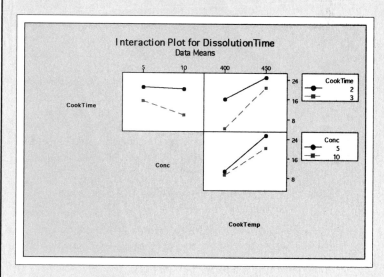

Figure 39 Interactions plot for gluten dissolution experiment.

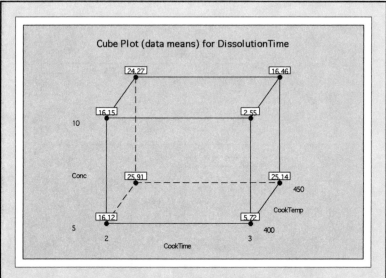

Figure 40 Cube plot for gluten dissolution experiment.

looking at the lower left hand corner, when the input factors combination is set at cook time of two minutes, concentration at five percent, and temperature at 450 degrees, an average dissolution time of 25.91 seconds is obtained. When the input factors combination is set at cook time of three minutes, concentration at 10 percent, and temperature at 400 degrees, an average dissolution time of 2.55 seconds is obtained. If we plan to conduct a follow-up experiment and our goal is to increase dissolution time, we may decide to select these settings (cook time two minutes, concentration five percent, and temperature 450 degrees) as the low settings for our inputs for the next experiment.

• *Review the statistical analysis.* Use Stat > DOE > Factorial > Analyze Factorial Design.

 – *Compare P value to alpha risk.* When a calculated P value is less than the alpha risk, it indicates that the factor is significant.

 – *Determine which factor is significant* (initially set P value at 0.10 and confidence level at 90 percent).

  o The effects plot (Figure 41) shows that only factors A (cook time), B (concentration), and C (cook temperature), and interactions AB (between cook time and concentration) and AC (between cook time and cook temperature)

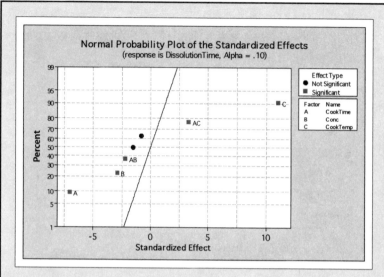

Figure 41   Normal probability plot for gluten dissolution
experiment at alpha = .10.

are significant at 90 percent confidence (alpha risk =
10 percent). These are represented by the squares on
the graph. Figure 41 also tells us that factors A, B, and
interaction AB have a negative effect on dissolution time
(shown to the left of the diagonal line) while factor C and
interaction AC have a positive effect on dissolution time
(shown to the right of the diagonal line). The further
away the square dots are from the diagonal line of
significance, the greater their effect on dissolution time.

o The Pareto chart (Figure 42) for effects also confirms
that only factors A, B, and C, and interactions AB and AC
are significant at 90 percent confidence (alpha risk = 10
percent). These are represented by the bars crossing the
cut-off line.

o Review the four-in-one graph of the residuals (Figure 43)
and look for patterns as discussed earlier. Looking at the
normal probability plot in Figure 43, the calculated
P value for residuals is 0.182, which is greater than the
alpha risk value of 0.10. Therefore, we conclude that the
residuals are normally distributed and are not significant.
The graph of residuals versus fits also shows no obvious
patterns.

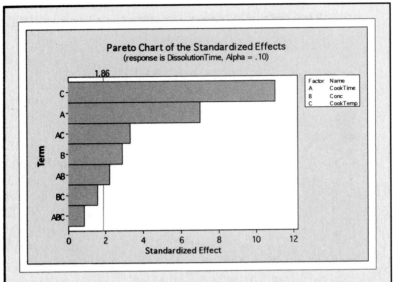

Figure 42 Pareto chart for gluten dissolution experiment at alpha = .10.

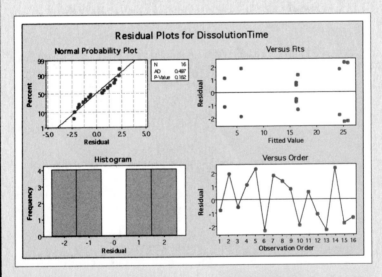

Figure 43 Four-in-one residuals graph for gluten dissolution experiment.

Table 6   Calculated P value for dissolution time.

Term	Calculated P value
Constant	0.000
CookTime	0.000
Conc	0.020
CookTemp	0.000
CookTime*Conc	0.059
CookTime*CookTemp	0.011
Conc*CookTemp	0.161
CookTime*Conc*CookTemp	0.432

○ From Table 6, looking at the calculated P values and comparing them against the alpha risk value of P = 0.10, we can state that only the two-way interaction Conc*CookTemp with P = .161 and three-way interaction CookTime*Conc*CookTemp with P = .432 are not significant. All other main effects and two-way interactions are significant at a 90 percent confidence level.

– Based on the results in Table 6, you can now drop the insignificant terms BC and ABC and rerun the analysis (reset P value to 0.05 and confidence level to 95 percent). The reason you are rerunning the analysis is to seek confirmation that the input factors and interactions that you found were significant at a 90 percent confidence level, are still significant at a 95 percent confidence level.

– Rerun the analysis using software and compare the calculated P value to 0.05. Only those factors that are less than 0.05 are significant. Be careful when dropping insignificant terms. The rule is: if a factor by itself is not significant but the interaction with another factor is significant, then you can not drop the main factor out of the analysis. Look at both the P value and R-sq (adjusted). Note: R-sq (adjusted) explains the amount of variation due to the influence of the selected input factors on the response (output).

○ From Figures 44 and 45, you can see that when the insignificant terms BC and ABC were removed and the analysis rerun at 95 percent confidence (alpha risk = five percent),

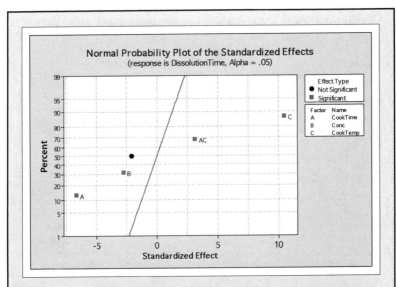

Figure 44 Normal probability plot for gluten dissolution experiment at alpha = .05 with factors A, B, AC, C, and AB.

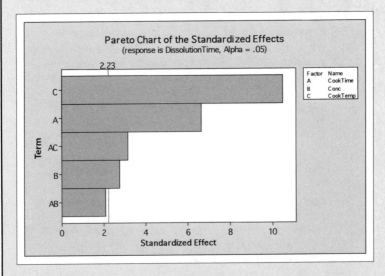

Figure 45 Pareto chart for gluten dissolution experiment rerun at alpha = .05 with factors C, A, AC, B, and AB.

Table 7   Calculated P value for dissolution time at alpha = 0.05.

Term	Calculated P value
Constant	0.000
CookTime	0.000
Conc	0.020
CookTemp	0.000
CookTime*Conc	0.063
CookTime*CookTemp	0.010

the two-way interaction AB now shows up as not being significant at 95 percent confidence. Note: While the effect of interaction AB (between cook time and concentration) on dissolution time showed up as being significant at a 90 percent confidence level, further analysis shows that it is not significant at the 95 percent confidence level. In other words, we can state with 95 percent confidence that the interaction effect between cook time and concentration has no significant impact on dissolution time.

o From Table 7, looking at the calculated P values and comparing them against the alpha risk value of P = .05, we can state that only the two-way interaction CookTime*Conc with P = .063 is not significant. All other main effects and two-way interactions are significant at a 95 percent confidence level.

– Based on the results in Table 7, you can now drop the insignificant terms AB and rerun the analysis. (Keep the P value at 0.05 and confidence level to 95 percent.) The reason you are rerunning the analysis is to seek confirmation that the input factors and interactions that you found were significant are still significant at a 95 percent confidence level after the interaction term AB is removed.

– Rerun analysis using software and compare the calculated P value to 0.05.

o Both effects charts (Figures 46 and 47) confirm that only main effects A, B, and C, and two-way interaction AC are significant with 95 percent confidence (alpha risk = five percent). An R-sq (adjusted) value of 89.47 percent means

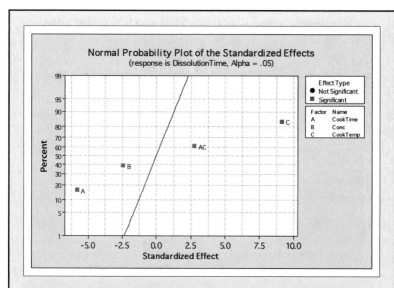

Figure 46 Normal probability plot for gluten dissolution experiment at alpha = .05 without interaction term AB.

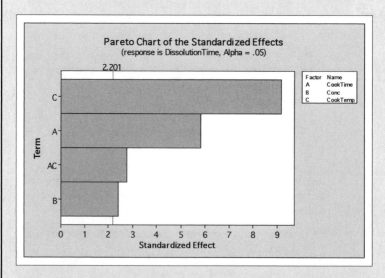

Figure 47 Pareto chart for gluten dissolution experiment at alpha = .05 without interaction term AB.

Table 8 Calculated P value for dissolution time at alpha = 0.05 without interaction term AB.

Term	Calculated P value
Constant	0.000
CookTime	0.000
Conc	0.035
CookTemp	0.000
CookTime*CookTemp	0.019

S = 2.79501, R-sq = 92.28%, R-sq(adj) = 89.47%

Analysis of variance for dissolution time

```
Source               DF   Seq SS  Adj SS   Adj MS      F      P
Main Effects          3   967.04  967.04  322.347  41.26  0.000
2-Way Interactions    1    59.44   59.44   59.444   7.61  0.019
Residual Error       11    85.93   85.93    7.812
  Lack of Fit         3    42.79   42.79   14.263   2.64  0.121
  Pure Error          8    43.14   43.14    5.393
Total                15  1112.42
```

Figure 48 Analysis of variance for dissolution time.

that 89.47 percent of the variation in the dissolution time is accounted for by the factors and interaction of factors shown in Table 8. We can now conclude with 95 percent confidence that dissolution time is impacted only by cook time, concentration, cook temperature, and the interaction between cook time and cook temperature.

o From the ANOVA table (Figure 48) we confirm with 95 percent confidence that the main effects are significant (low P value—0.000). The two-way interaction is significant (low P value—0.019) and the lack of fit of the prediction equation is not significant (high P value—0.121).

o From Table 9, the prediction equation for dissolution time is: Dissolution time = 96.9025 – 73.6800 (CookTime) – 0.673000 (Concentration) – 0.129300 (CookTemp) + 0.154200 (CookTime*CookTemp).

Table 9   Estimated coefficients for dissolution time using data in uncoded units (data for prediction equation from software).

Term	Coef
Constant	96.9025
CookTime	−73.6800
Conc	−0.673000
CookTemp	−0.129300
CookTime*CookTemp	0.154200

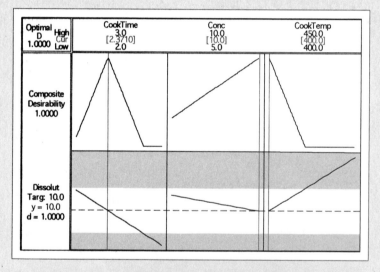

Figure 49   Response optimizer graph for gluten dissolution experiment.

- *Use the response optimizer* (Stat > DOE > Factorial > Response Optimizer). If you wanted to find the input factor settings for a target dissolution time of 10 seconds, then cook time must be set at 2.371 minutes, concentration set at 10 percent, and cook temperature set at 400 degrees (see Figure 49).

EXAMPLE 15
DESIGN OF EXPERIMENTS: PELLET HARDNESS

A manufacturer wanted to determine the important factors affecting hardness of a pellet. The input factors chosen for the study were:

Pressure (lbs)	Time (minutes)	Binder (%)
2500	2	10
3000	3	12

Response (output) = Pellet hardness

This experiment was set up as a three-factor design, with each factor having two levels, or a low and high setting. The experimenter chooses to run the experiment with two replicates, namely, two experimental runs with the same factor settings (levels). For example, the factor setting combination of pressure 2500 pounds, time two minutes, and binder 10 percent is replicated (see Table 10).

Table 10 Experimental worksheet and results—pellet hardness.

Pressure (lbs)	Time (minutes)	Binder (%)	Hardness
2500	2	10	7.392
3000	2	10	9.456
2500	3	10	8.988
3000	3	10	18.084
2500	2	12	15.000
3000	2	12	7.734
2500	3	12	15.792
3000	3	12	15.606
2500	2	10	8.082
3000	2	10	13.422
2500	3	10	7.734
3000	3	10	19.356
2500	2	12	16.788
3000	2	12	9.312
2500	3	12	15.42
3000	3	12	16.536

The experiment was conducted and pellet hardness recorded for each combination of input factor settings. Data were analyzed using a software package.

- *Review the graphical analyses.*

  - *Main effects plot.* Use Stat > DOE > Factorial > Factorial Plots. The *y*-axis in Figure 50 represents pellet hardness and the *x*-axis on each graph shows the low setting and high setting for each input factor. The two black dots within each graph represent the average pellet hardness value obtained at the low and high settings for that input factor. All three factors—pressure, time, and binder—have an effect on the pellet hardness (see Figure 50). We can also see that a lower pellet hardness value is obtained when the input factor values are set at the low end, and a higher pellet hardness value is obtained when the input factor values are set at the high end.

  - *Interactions plot.* Use Stat > ANOVA > Interaction Plot (Figure 51). There is no interaction between binder and time. However, there is an interaction between binder and pressure at the high-end settings as well as time and pressure at the low-end settings.

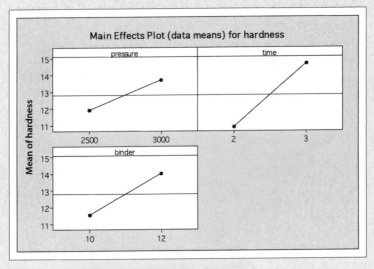

Figure 50   Main effects plot for pellet hardness experiment.

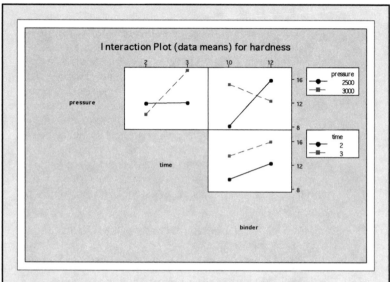

Figure 51 Interactions plot for pellet hardness experiment.

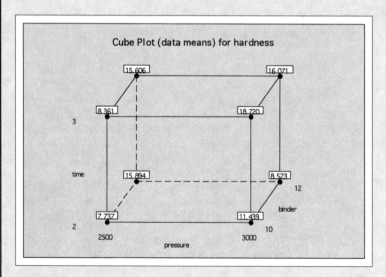

Figure 52 Cube plot for pellet hardness experiment.

– *Review the factorial plot.* Use Stat > DOE > Factorial > Factorial Plots. The cube plot (Figure 52) shows the relationship between the input factors and pellet hardness.

The figure at each corner is the average pellet hardness for that combination of settings. For the pellet hardness data, looking at the lower left hand corner, when the input factors combination is set at pressure of 2500 pounds, binder at 10 percent, and time at two minutes, an average pellet hardness of 7.737 is obtained. When the input factors combination is set at pressure of 3000 lbs, binder at 10 percent, and time at three minutes, an average pellet hardness of 18.720 is obtained. If we plan to conduct a follow-up experiment and our goal is to increase pellet hardness, we may decide to select these settings (pressure 3000 lbs, binder 10 percent, and time three minutes) as the low settings for our inputs for the next experiment.

- *Review the statistical analysis.* Use Stat > DOE > Factorial > Analyze Factorial Design.

  - *Compare P value to alpha risk.* When a calculated P value is less than the alpha risk, it indicates that the factor is significant.

  - *Determine which factor is significant* (initially set P value at 0.10 and confidence level at 90 percent).

    o The effects plot (Figure 53) shows that only factors A (pressure), B (time), and C (binder), and interactions AB (between pressure and time) and AC (between pressure and binder) are significant at 90 percent confidence (alpha risk = 10 percent). These are represented by the square dots on the graph. The graph also tells us that interaction AC has a negative effect (lowers hardness) on pellet hardness (left of the blue line) while factors A, B, and C, and interaction AB have a positive effect (increase hardness) on pellet hardness. The further away the square dots are from the diagonal line of significance, the greater their effect on pellet hardness.

    o The Pareto chart for effects (Figure 54) also shows that only factors A, B, and C, and interactions AB and AC are significant at 90 percent confidence (alpha risk = 10 percent). These are represented by the bars crossing the cut-off line.

    o Review the four-in-one graph of the residuals (Figure 55) and look for patterns as discussed earlier. Residuals are normally distributed with no obvious patterns.

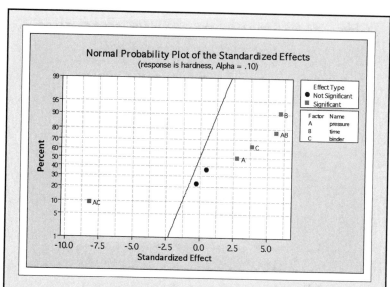

Figure 53 Normal probability plot for pellet hardness experiment at alpha = .10.

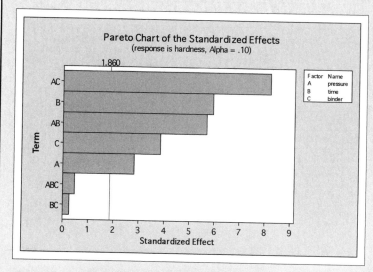

Figure 54 Pareto chart for pellet hardness experiment at alpha = .10.

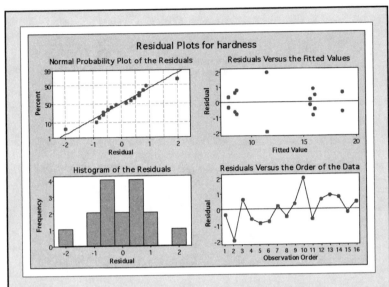

Figure 55   Four-in-one residuals graph for pellet hardness experiment.

Table 11   Calculated P value for pellet hardness at alpha = 0.10.

Term	Calculated P value
Constant	0.000
Pressure	0.023
Time	0.000
Binder	0.005
Pressure*Time	0.000
Pressure*Binder	0.000
Time*Binder	0.807
Pressure*Time*Binder	0.657
S = 1.27686, R-sq = 95.18%, R-sq(adj) = 90.96%	

- From Table 11, looking at the calculated P values and comparing them against the alpha risk value of P = 0.10, we can state that only the two-way interaction Time*Binder with P = .807 and three-way interaction Pressure*Time*Binder with P = .657 are not significant.

All other main effects and two-way interactions are significant at a 90 percent confidence level.

- Based on the results above, you can now drop the insignificant terms ABC and BC and rerun the analysis. (Reset P value to 0.05 and confidence level to 95 percent.) The reason you are rerunning the analysis is to seek confirmation that the input factors and interactions that you found were significant at a 90 percent confidence level are still significant at a 95 percent confidence level.

- Rerun the analysis using software and compare the calculated P value to 0.05. Only those factors that are less than 0.05 are significant. Be careful when dropping insignificant terms. The rule is: if a factor by itself is not significant but the interaction with another factor is significant, then you can not drop the main factor out of the analysis. Look at both the P value and R-sq (adjusted). Note: R-sq (adjusted) explains the amount of variation due to the influence of the selected input factors on the response (output).

  o Both effects charts (Figures 56 and 57) confirm that only main effects A, B, and C, and two-way interactions AB

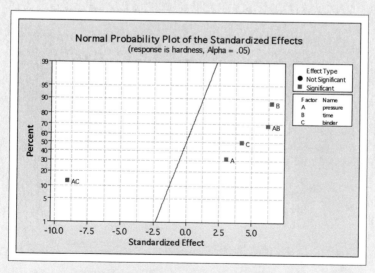

Figure 56 Normal probability plot for pellet hardness experiment at alpha = .05.

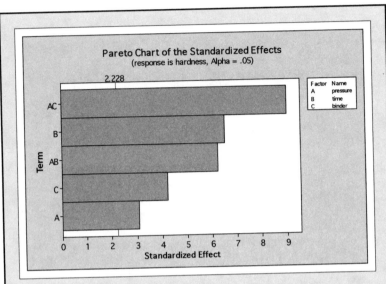

Figure 57 Pareto chart of effects for pellet hardness experiment at alpha = .05.

and AC are significant with 95 percent confidence (alpha risk = five percent).

o An R-sq (adjusted) value of 92.51 percent means that 92.51 percent of the variation in the pellet hardness is accounted for by the selected input factors (see Table 12). We can now conclude with 95 percent confidence that pellet hardness is impacted only by pressure, time, binder, and the interaction between pressure and time, and pressure and binder.

o From the ANOVA table (Figure 58) we confirm with 95 percent confidence that the main effects are significant (low P value—0.000), the two-way interaction is significant (low P value—0.000), and the lack of fit of the prediction equation is not significant (high P value—.873).

o From Table 13, the prediction equation for pellet hardness is: Pellet hardness = −237.535 + 0.0826635 (Pressure) − 36.0645 (Time) + 30.0592 (Binder) + 0.0144930 (Pressure*Time) − 0.0104835 (Pressure*Binder)

Table 12   Calculated P value for pellet hardness at alpha = 0.05 without interaction terms ABC and BC.

Term	Calculated P value
Constant	0.000
Pressure	0.012
Time	0.000
Binder	0.002
Pressure*Time	0.000
Pressure*Binder	0.000

S = 1.16166, R-sq = 95.01%, R-sq(adj) = 92.51%

Analysis of Variance for hardness (coded units)

```
Source               DF    Seq SS    Adj SS    Adj MS      F        P
Main Effects          3    94.484    94.484   31.4948   23.34    0.000
2-Way Interactions    2   162.416   162.416   81.2078   60.18    0.000
Residual Error       10    13.495    13.495    1.3495
  Lack of Fit         2     0.452     0.452    0.2258    0.14    0.873
  Pure Error          8    13.043    13.043    1.6304
Total                15   270.395
```

Figure 58   Analysis of variance for hardness (coded units).

Table 13   Estimated coefficients for hardness using data in uncoded units (data for prediction equation from software).

Term	Coef
Constant	−237.535
Pressure	0.0826635
Time	−36.0645
Binder	30.0592
Pressure*time	0.0144930
Pressure*binder	−0.0104835

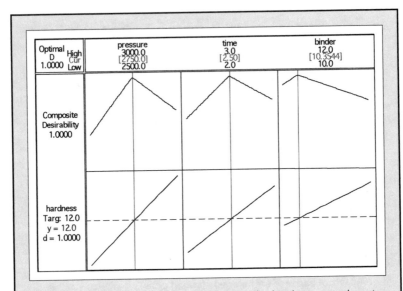

Figure 59 Response optimizer graph for pellet hardness experiment.

- *Use the response optimizer* (Stat > DOE > Factorial > Response Optimizer). If you wanted to find the input factor settings for a target pellet hardness of 12, then set pressure at 2750 pounds, time at 2.5 minutes, and binder at 10.3544 percent (see Figure 59).

END OF IMPROVE PHASE

You have now reached the end of the Improve phase in the DMAIC process improvement methodology.

- Use the End of Improve Phase Checklist to ensure that all of the Improve phase activities have been completed.

- Collect objective evidence for items on the checklist and use them as a guide to present management with monthly updates.

- Follow good record keeping practice (whatever method works for your organization, electronic or hard copy).

- Update your action item list that you created in the Measure phase with information from all the DOEs. Note: You now know what input factors are significant and not significant to your process. The significant factors need to be controlled to ensure that your process behaves in a consistent fashion.

End of Improve Phase Checklist		
Items	**Place (✓) in box to indicate completion**	**Comments**
DOE		
• Input factors (X's)		
• Output factor (Y)		
• P values for significant factors		
• R-sq adjusted		
• Residuals OK?		
• Which factor or interaction is significant		
• Main effects plot		
• Interaction plot		
Did you run a gage R&R before DOE data collection?		
• Gage R&R value		
• Number of distinct categories		
Response optimizer		
• Mathematical model		
Communication plan being followed		
Meeting held with management		
• Roadblocks encountered		
Note: you may run multiple DOEs if results warrant.		

V

Control

PURPOSE OF CONTROL PHASE

You are now entering the last phase of the DMAIC process improvement methodology. The DMAIC process is similar to what happens when a patient visits the hospital. At first, the physician has the patient describe the problem they are experiencing by asking questions regarding their health (Define phase). Then they take baseline readings with tests such as blood tests, urinalysis, electrocardiograph (ECG) tests, and so on (Measure phase). The physician then prescribes medication and asks the patient to try it out and return for ongoing visits (Analyze phase). During the return visits, tests are run to ensure/confirm that the medication is working and the diagnosis is correct (Improve phase). When the patient is improving, the physician reruns the blood tests, urinalysis, and ECG, to ensure that all vital signs are stable, and finally the patient is discharged (Control phase).

To draw a parallel, the process improvement team is playing the role of the "physician" while the process undergoing improvement is the "patient." Once you have reduced the "hemorrhage"—the number of defects that your process was making—you can state that you have found a solution to your problem. The process improvement team was a process doctor, taking the process through all the stages leading to a diagnosis in the Improve phase. You now know the mathematical model of relationships between the significant inputs and the impact they have on the output. Armed with this knowledge, you are now ready to enter into the Control phase: to place controls on all those significant input factors that influence the output.

MONITOR THE STABILITY OF THE PROCESS— STATISTICAL PROCESS CONTROL

Statistical process control (SPC) is to a process what an ECG is to a patient; SPC measures the critical characteristics of the process and its output on a real-time basis and places the power in the hands of the employees to take action if something were to go out of control. It measures the stability of the process. There are many books and software programs that are available that describe how to set up an SPC program and how to interpret the chart; however, you must know the appropriate chart to be used based on the data type that you are collecting. Table 14 provides you with guidelines for chart selection based on data type.

All SPC charts have some basic elements such as the average line, the upper control limit, the lower control limit, and the individual data points plotted. Each individual data point represents a measure of the characteristic being checked, for example, a dimension, the number of defects, number of instances failed during a QC check. The upper and lower control limits are calculated values, each three standard deviations away from the centerline.

One point to remember is to stop and determine what happened if a single point falls outside the control limits, known as special cause variation. Why is this? You might already know that in a standard normal distribution, 99.73 percent of all data falls within ±3 standard deviations from the mean or average. Therefore, the probability of any point falling outside the control limits is 0.27 percent, or 0.0135 percent on each side. This indicates a special cause indeed, and warrants stopping to find out what happened. However, for attribute data or count data charts, any point falling outside the lower control limit suggests that something has improved in the process, and the process produces fewer defectives or defects. You must learn what happened and try to emulate the situation.

Table 14   SPC chart selection based on type of data.

Variable/ continuous data	Attribute data	Count data
$\overline{X}$ and R chart, used when subgroup size ≤ 10	*np* chart; base size is fixed and you are plotting the actual number of defects for each lot checked	*c* chart; base size is fixed and you are plotting the actual count of defects per lot checked
$\overline{X}$ and *s* chart, used when subgroup size >10	*p* chart; base size varies and you can convert to proportion defective per lot and then plot the proportion defective value	*u* chart; base size varies and you are plotting the average number of defects per unit for each lot checked

EXAMPLE 16
SPC CHARTS

Variable Data (Stat> Control Chart > Variable Chart for Subgroup > X bar - R)

Every hour six parts were taken from a stamping machine and verified for flatness. The subgroup size is six. The data were plotted in the form of an $\bar{X}$ and R chart (Figure 60).

Count Data (Stat> Control Charts > Attribute Chart > C Chart)

A customer service department documented the number of missed calls for every 100 calls received. Data were collected over 100 days and plotted in the form of a c chart (Figure 61). Note: The lower control limit in the c chart is zero. Ideally, the customer service department would like to have no missed calls.

Attribute Data (Stat> Control Charts > Attribute Chart > P Chart)

The finance department of a company captured data on the number of hours it took to process invoices for payment. The data were entered in

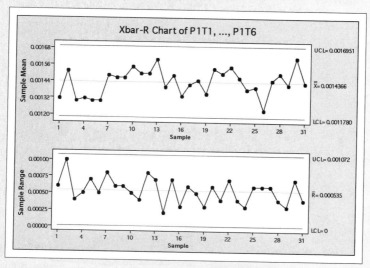

Figure 60 $\bar{X}$ and R chart of stamping machine data.

two columns, one showing time in days and the other showing the number of invoices processed. Note that in the *p* chart (Figure 62), the upper and lower control limits are continually recalculated since the number of invoices processed changes over the duration checked.

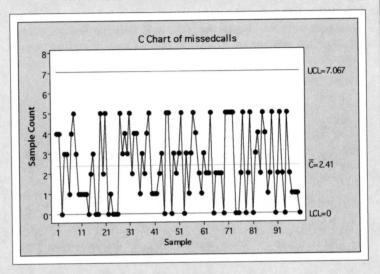

Figure 61   *c* chart of missed call data.

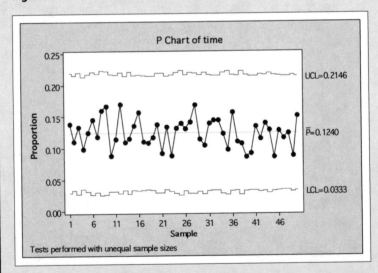

Figure 62   *p* chart of invoice processing time data.

MISTAKE-PROOFING/POKA-YOKE

Mistake-proofing, also known as *poka-yoke*, is a technique used to error-proof a process to prevent defects from being made or being sent out to the customer. How do you know what step in your process needs to be error-proofed? The FMEA is a good guide, since it identifies the step(s) in the process that are the riskiest. If you have a step with a high severity number or a step with a high occurrence number combined with a low detection number, these are flags telling you to redesign the step or place better controls on that step to prevent the error from being made or being passed on to the next step.

Mistake-proofing may include activities such as designing a fixture to ensure proper orientation for assembly, designing a checklist, utilizing menus in software that preclude you from performing an activity if an incorrect number is entered in a field, installing an alarm that is triggered when something goes wrong, and so on. It is an activity that involves input from the process improvement team. The mistake-proofing device, after being constructed, is usually piloted and checked to make sure it is working as intended. Mistake-proofing devices encourage creativity before capital; in many instances a low-cost solution can get the job done just as well as an expensive system.

TECHNOLOGY TRANSFER—THE CONTROL PLAN

You are now ready to send the patient home with a prescription and dietary guidelines. A document that plays a similar role for our process is called the *control plan*. Since there are many books written about how to create control plans, the description here will be kept at a relatively high level. There are three important documents relating to your process. They are the process map, the FMEA, and the control plan. The control plan is also created with input from the team, utilizing the other two critical documents.

Creating a control plan (see Figure 63):

- The first step in the process map must be the first step in the FMEA and also the first step in the control plan. Copy the steps from the process map into the control plan verbatim, that is, the first step, second step, third step, and so on.

- For each step described, identify the equipment used in that step. The equipment can be a computer, software program, or machine, as appropriate. These are the X's in your process map that you have identified as equipment used in that step.

		Characteristics					Methods					
Part/ process number	Process name/ operation description	Device, jig, tools, for mfg.	No.	Product	Process	Special char. class	Product/ process specification/ tolerance	Evaluation/ measurement technique	Sample		Control method	Reaction plan
									Size	Freq.		
00	Receipt of material		i	1008 CR ETP, T-5CA	Receiving		.0094 ± .0005	Micrometer and caliper review certificates and visual inspection	One coil	Every lot	Receiving inspection per WI 7.51, supplier material certificates, and visual inspection	Reject per applicable procedures. Notify customer. RTV for credit or replacement of material.
10	Preparation of tool for manufacturing		ii		Visual inspection		Cutting edges, worn out punches	Visual examination	One	Each die	Inspection of each sample	Return die to tool room for correction.
20	Set up progressive		iii	Finished parts	Setup inspection		Dimensional and visual inspection per inspection plan	Standard measurement instruments	2 pcs/ Tk	Every setup	First-piece inspection per quality inspection plan, customer drawing, and applicable procedures.	Reject setup and return to manufacturing for adjustments. Notify setup operator and tool and die maker for correction.
30	Stamping progressive		1	Window location	Production inspection	KC-1	.4724 + .0000/ –.004	Hub datum Gage #9000-27	2/Tk	Hour	In-process inspection plan, customer drawing, SPC	Segregate defective product. Notify QA for processing of nonconforming product per applicable procedures.
			2	Center hole diameter		Cr	.1615 + .001/ –.002	Go/no-go plug gages	2/Tk	2x per shift	In-process inspection plan, customer drawing, applicable work instructions and operating procedures.	Make necessary adjustments. Verify applicable characteristics.
			3	Flatness		KC-2	Within .0035	Dial test indicator	2/Tk	Hour	Documented by operator twice per shift. Audit by QA.	

Continued

Figure 63   Example of a control plan for a stamping process.

Part/ process number	Process name/ operation description	Device, jig, tools, for mfg.	Characteristics					Methods					Reaction plan
			No.	Product	Process	Special char. class	Product/ process specification/ tolerance	Evaluation/ measurement technique	Sample		Control method	
									Size	Freq.		
			4	Height		KC-3	.062 ± .002	Hub datum gage #9000-26	3/Tk	Hour		Continue production after correction of nonconformance.
			5	T.I.R.		KC-4	Within .003	Hub datum gage #9000-26	3/Tk	Hour		
			6	Visual inspection		Cr	Watch for dents, cupping, pitted surface, heavy burrs, missing features, cracks, and so on.	Visual inspection	3/Tk	Every 3000 pcs.		
			7	Burr height		Cr	Within .002	Dial test indicator	2/Tk	Every bag		

Figure 63 *Continued.*

- Identify any characteristics that are being checked (quality control) in this step. These are the distinguishing features, dimensions, or properties.

- Enter any cross-reference number from the process map, FMEA, blueprint, customer order, and so on.

- Enter significant features of the product or service for this step. Information can be gathered from customer requirements or drawings. If not applicable, state NA.

- Enter any special characteristic classifications from the process map. Use the appropriate classification to designate the characteristic or leave the field blank. If in doubt, look at the flowchart to determine if it is a critical or noise variable.

- Product/process specifications/tolerances can be obtained from drawings, DOE, material data, or customer/organization requirements.

- Evaluation/measurement technique: identify the measuring system being used. Include gage R&R data, equipment type, acceptance criteria, and so on.

- Sample size/frequency: when sampling is required, state the sample size and frequency.

- Control method: if using SPC, state the type of chart being used.

- Reaction plan: specifies necessary corrective actions should things go wrong. Typically the responsibility of the person closest to the process.

Repeat this for every step in your process until the control plan is completed. The control plan now has all the information about the process.

WRAP-UP—UPDATING ESSENTIAL DOCUMENTS

Before you can claim that the project has been completed, there are some essential documents that need to be updated. These are the documents that you started out with in the Measure phase of your process improvement project. They are the process map, the FMEA, process capability, and gage R&R:

- The process map needs to be updated with all the inputs that you have identified as being critical to the process, based on regression equations, ANOVA values, and DOE values. These are the inputs where the results had low P values.

- The FMEA needs to be updated with the action items completed and new risk priority number calculations.

- Process capability needs to be recalculated. For variable data this means looking at the process performance after improvement, with respect to customer calculations. The process capability should have improved from the baseline. For attribute and count data it is a recalculation of the yield of the process after improvement. Yield in both cases must have improved.

- Gage R&R must be performed after retraining if the original gage R&R values were not acceptable. The new gage R&R values may be cross-referenced in the control plan.

- Other documents that you may create or update include standard operating procedures, training documents, and audit plans.

CALCULATING PROJECT SAVINGS

Each organization has its own rules for calculating project savings. Since you started out by quantifying the number of rejects—using process capability—at the start of your process improvement project (in the Measure phase), it goes without saying that the recalculated process capability at the end of the project (in the Control phase) should show a reduction of same. The reduction in the number of rejects can be converted into savings in material costs, labor costs, overhead costs, rework costs, and so on.

You may wish to talk to your finance department first and provide them with the hard numbers and let them assist you in arriving at the dollar figure. Savings are only annualized; that is, you can not claim recurring savings year after year.

FINAL REPORT

As a team, create a final report regarding the project. The final report need not be elaborate, but simply contain all the critical pieces of information from each of the DMAIC phases.

You can take the final checklists from the end of each of the phases, together with their artifacts, and use them as your final report. An executive summary, usually one page long, is a must. This provides the problem statement, objectives, and the achievement by the team. Do not forget to acknowledge all team members on the project. And last but not least, do not forget to celebrate the team's hard work on the project.

END OF CONTROL PHASE

You have now reached the end of the Control phase in the DMAIC process improvement methodology:

- Use the End of Control Phase Checklist to ensure that all of the Control phase activities have been completed.

- Collect objective evidence for items on the checklist and use them as a guide to present management with monthly updates.

- Follow good record keeping practice (whatever method works for your organization, electronic or hard copy).

End of Control Phase Checklist		
Items	**Place (✓) in box to indicate completion**	**Comments**
SPC • *p* chart • *np* chart • *c* chart • *u* chart • $\bar{X}$ and *R* chart • $\bar{X}$ and *s* chart		
Mistake-proofing		
Control plan		
Essential documents updated • Process map • FMEA • Process capability • Gage R&R • Procedures • Training plans • Audit plans		
Project savings calculated • Raw data provided to finance • Dollar savings calculated by finance		
Communication plan being followed		
Meeting held with management • Roadblocks encountered		
Final report completed		
Note: Don't forget to celebrate		

Index

A

alpha risk (α), 42
  in DOE, 74, 86
alternate hypothesis (H_a), 42
analysis of variance (ANOVA), 53–64
  assumptions (table), 55
  in DOE, 67
  steps, 54–55
Analyze, phase of DMAIC
    methodology, 41–65
  purpose of, 41
Anderson-Darling normality test, 58
attribute data, 20
  calculating process sigma for, 27
  in SPC, 97–98

B

Bartlett's test, in ANOVA, 58

C

c chart, in SPC, 97
central tendency, measures of, 20
characterization designs, in DOE, 68
coefficient of determination (R-sq), 51
  in ANOVA, 55, 61
  in DOE, 79–81, 89, 90

communication plan, 6
components of variation, in gage
    R&R, 31
conformance costs, 2
continuous improvement (CI)
    methodologies, types, xv–xvi
Control, phase of DMAIC
    methodology, 95–104
  purpose of, 95
control plan, 99–102
  example, *100*
correlation test, 48–49
  examples, 49, 50
  in Minitab, example, 51–52
cost of good quality, (COGQ), 2
cost of quality (COQ), 2
cost of poor quality (COPQ), 2
count data, 20
  calculating process sigma for, 27
  in SPC, 97
C_p (process capability), calculating,
    23, 26
C_{pk} (process capability), calculating,
    23–24, 26
customer requirements, xvi–xvii

D

data
  summarizing, 20–21